FOOT
CROSS

1st SEASON

Thomas Trickett
Publications Ltd

First published in 1994
by THOMAS TRICKETT PUBLICATIONS LTD
23 Balmoral Road, Poole, Dorset, BH14 8TJ

The Thomas Trickett character was created by cartoonist Kim Leachman for Thomas Trickett Publications Ltd ©1994

ISBN 0 9524483 0 0

Printed in England
by Roman Press Limited, Bournemouth

Acknowledgements

We would like to express our thanks to Chris Dancer for his invaluable artwork

Special thanks are due to Tina Llewellyn and Nathalie Antonia for their unstinted assistance in the production of this book and our debt to Ieuan, the inspiration behind Thomas Trickett, is gratefully acknowledged

Thomas Trickett Publications Ltd

Foreword

For several years I have compiled and provided football crosswords for Football League matchday programmes.

Now for the enjoyment of football lovers everywhere here is my Football Crossword Book.

Good Luck,

Thomas Trickett

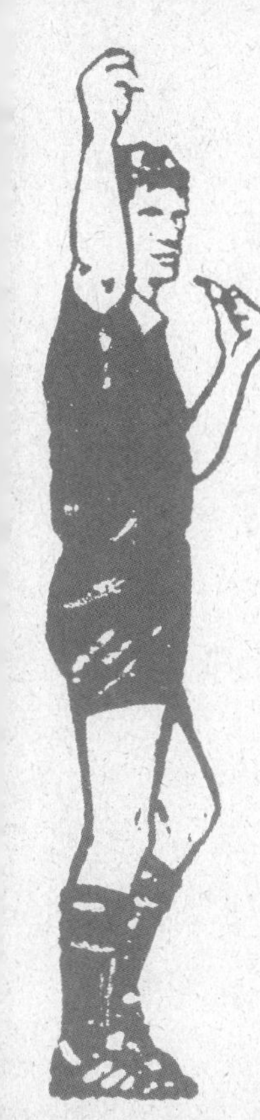

KICK OFF

1

Across

1. Extra player on stand-by. 10
8. Ray Gill made 408 appearances for this English club 1951/62. 7
9. Rovers side found in Scotland. 5
10. Portman _ _ _ _, Ipswich Town FC. 4
11. Half a circle situated at the edge of the area. 4
12. You never walked alone in this end at Anfield. 3
14. Relegated English Premier League 1993/94. 6
15. World Cup winners 1958, 1962, 1970 & 1994. 6
18. FA Cup is a knock _ _ _ competition. 3
20. Football hooligan. 4
21. Forename of European Footballer of the Year 1961. 4
23. Johnny, former W.B.A. manager. 5
24. Paul Van Himst managed this national side USA 94. 7
25. Ex-Manchester United boss. 4 & 6

Down

1. Attendant often seen at soccer games. 7
2. Non-League team who play at Twerton Park. 4
3. Home country of football club, Galatasary. 6
4. The _ _ _ _ _ _ _ _, Huddersfield Town's nickname. 8
5. Magic hat for three goals. 5
6. The McCain Stadium is this team's home. 11
7. Club nickname of Plymouth Argyle. 3 & 8
13. Peter Beardsley once played for this Cumbrian side. 8
16. Sadly, this African squad died in an air crash 1993. 7
17. Forever blow one in a song at Upton Park. 6
19. League of Ireland, Shelbourne FC, play at this park. 5
22. No bumps on this kind of football pitch. 4

1

■	■	1		2		3		4		5		■
6	■		■		■		■		■		■	7
8							■	9				
	■		■		■		■		■		■	
10				■	11				■	12		
	■		■	13	■		■		■	■	■	
14						■	15			16		
	■	■	■		■	17	■		■		■	
18		19	■	20				■	21			
	■		■		■		■	22	■		■	
23					■	24						
	■		■		■		■		■		■	
■	25										■	■

2

Across

1. Soccer sides are mates. (anag) 5
4. Top of the table collision. 5
10. Gamblers check them every Saturday. 5
11. Flags are raised when a player is caught. 7
12. Draw level. 8
13. Penalty _ _ _ _ . 4
15. Club nickname of Swindon Town. 6
17. Lee, a very acute footballer. 6
19. _ _ _ _ Ruddock, English Premier League player. 4
20. Non-League Essex side, _ _ _ _ _ _ _ _ & Redbridge. 8
23. European national side. 7
24. Russell, former England defender. 5
25. Drink container seen at many a cold match. 5
26. _ _ _ _ _ Welch, English League goalkeeper. 5

Down

2. Efan, Nigerian striker. 5
3. Altrincham play here. 4 & 4
5. Sincil Bank team. (abbrev) 4
6. Fit captain. 7
7. Bobby Charlton made 106 for England. 11
8. Paolo, European Footballer of the Year 1982. 5
9. World Cup winners 1954. 4 & 7
14. Liverpool v Everton 1986 FA Cup final result. 5 & 3
16. City side found at Ashton Gate. 7
18. Asian national side. 5
21. Paul Van _ _ _ _ _ , Belgium manager USA 1994. 5
22. In early days, they were changed after each goal. 4

2

■	1	2		3		■	4	5		6		■
7	■		■		■	8	■		■		■	9
10					■	11						
	■		■		■		■		■		■	
12								■	13			
	■	■	■		■		■	14	■		■	
15		16				■	17					
	■		■		■	18	■		■	■	■	
19				■	20					21		
	■		■	22	■		■		■		■	
23							■	24				
	■		■		■		■		■		■	
■	25					■	26					■

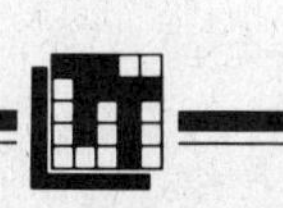

3

Across

1. Shaun and the FA can make a striker. (anag) 7
7. Bulgarian side, CSKA. 5
8. Nationality of defender, Franco Baresi. 7
9. Ian, England striker. 6
11. An out game in the FA Cup. 5
13. & 5. down. Burnley play here. 4 & 4
14. Footwear item for soccer coach. 7
15. 90 minutes of drama. 4
16. Below a hill at Barnet's stadium. 5
17. Marco Van _ _ _ _ _ _ . 6
21. Non-League club, Windsor _ _ _ _ _ _ _ . 3 & 4
22. Distances in which football pitches are measured. 5
23. Roy, USA international. 7

Down

2. European Super Cup winners 1982/83. 5 & 5
3. Andy Davidson appeared 520 times for this English League club 1952/67. 4 & 4
4. Phil, former Liverpool and England international. 4
5. see 13. across.
6. Pop concert at Bury. 4
9. _ _ _ _ _ Clarke, Sniffer's younger brother. 5
10. Cyril Knowles managed this north of England club. 10
12. Former Liverpool manager. 5
13. This side play at Prenton Park. 8
18. Bachelor party at Mansfield. (nick) 4
19. _ _ _ _ Goey, Dutch international goalkeeper. 2 & 2
20. Gascoigne injured his, in English FA Cup final 1991. 4

3

Across

1. Nickname of Yorkshire side who won the FA Cup 1912. 5
7. Barry Kitchener appeared a record 523 times for this London club 1967/82. 8
8. Former England manager. 5
10. Home of "The Canaries". 6 & 4
12. Club nickname of Bolton Wanderers. 8
14. Northern Irish League club. 4
16. Gambling chances for the match. 4
17. Same ending for Charlton and Oldham. 8
20. Brian Little once managed this English club. 10
23. Elected to Division 4 1978. 5
24. Park here for Middlesbrough. 8
25. Forename of "The Posh". 5

Down

1. If keeper is missing, the goal becomes an open one. 6
2. Frenchman, _ _ _ _ Cantona. 4
3. On the terrace, one of many to stand on. 4
4. Knocks for the ref's whistle. 5
5. This side is certainly not the underdog. 9
6. Club nickname of Sheffield United. 6
9. Some say World Cup is the greatest show on _ _ _ _ _ . 5
11. Edgy players at Berwick. (nick) 9
13. Find a rodent in Fratton Park. 3
15. Referees view use of this as illegal. 5
16. This team's previous ground was Sheepfoot Lane. 6
18. Not a goal-kick, but still a kick. 6
19. Winner of this Division gains promotion to Premier. 5
21. Footballers keep fit at these places. 4
22. Striker's number for old system centre-forward. 4

4

5

Across

6. Sir Bobby's famous brother. 4 & 8
8. Club nickname of Luton Town. 7
9. Football exam expecially for youngsters. 5
10. League of Ireland side, _ _ _ _ Wanderers. 4
12. Pavel Sadyrin managed this national side USA 1994. 6
14. Soccer kit that has been known to tease. 5
15. & 3. down. England star of the early 1970s. 6 & 5
16. The _ _ _ _ , Dunfermline Athletic. (nick) 4
19. Robbie, English Premier League striker. 5
21. Partick v Hearts 1959 League Cup Final result. 3 & 4
22. The O's. 6 & 6

Down

1. Country of birth of Ray Houghton. 8
2. Drill back the ball. 5
3. See 15. across.
4. Danish player. 7
5. Finnish League club, Jazz _ _ _ _ . 4
6. Jamaican-born English Premier League striker. 4 & 6
7. No goals against and the goalie has kept this. 5 & 5
11. Pig's abode in Alexandra's Gresty Road. 3
12. Graham, former Arsenal player of the early 1980's. 3
13. Singular Blackpool player. (nick) 8
14. Position Wednesday finished 1993-94 season. 7
17. One for a draw. 5
18. Mr Neill, former Arsenal boss. 5
20. Forename of English Premier League striker, Mr Fox. 4

5

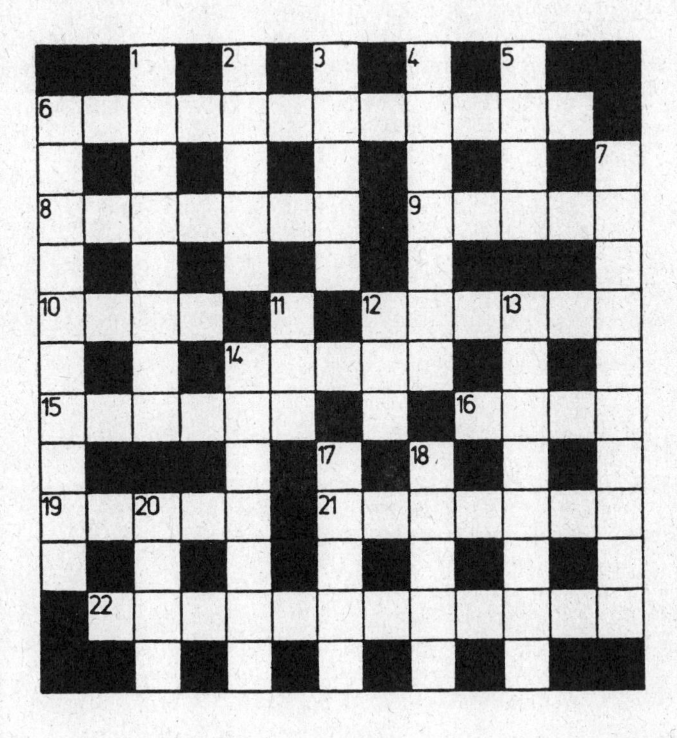

6

Across

3. County side Mike Summerbee once managed. 9
8. Find a manager's responsiblilty in his win bonuses. 4
9. Players should score if target is like this. 4 & 4
10. Underground passage at Wembley. 6
13. Nationality of Frank Rijkaard. 5
14. Watch the match from here. 7
15. Gavin _ _ _cock. 3
16. Home of "The Saddlers". 7
17. Bob Morton played 494 games for this English club. 5
21. Alf Ramsey's courageous World Cup team. 6
22. David, English Premier League player. 8
23. Peruvian Indian found here in Cambridge United. 4
24. See this team play at the Victoria Ground. 5 & 4

Down

1. League side in N. Ireland. 9
2. Twist here to enter the ground. 9
4. Implements such as West Ham United nickname. 5
5. "The Blues". 7
6. Louis, former England and Burnley winger. 4
7. Gresty _ _ _ _ , Crewe Alexandra's ground. 4
11. The home of W.B.A. 9
12. One of seven at Hillsborough. 9
14. _ _ _ Venables. (short) 3
15. Synthetic playing surface. 7
18. Unfair players try to do this. 5
19. _ _ _ _ s Hall, Southend United. 4
20. Paul Gascoigne once wore one due to facial injury. 4

6

1	■	2	■	3	4		5		6		7	
8				■		■		■		■		■
	■		■	■	9							
10						■		■		■		■
	■		■	■		■		■	■	11	■	12
13					■	14						
	■		■	■	15			■	■		■	
16							■	17				
	■		■	■		■	18	■	■		■	
■	19	■	20	■		■	21					
22								■	■		■	
■		■		■		■		■	23			
24									■		■	

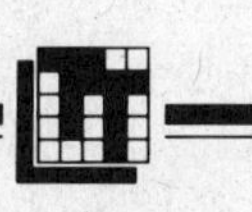

7

Across

1. Wattie Moore played a record 447 times for this English club 1948/64. 10
8. Old-fashioned accessories for football fans. 7
9. Enzo, Belgian international. 5
10. Vessels worth winning. 4
11. Foul journey on the pitch. 4
12. Youngster found in "The Blades" team, apparently. 3
14. Country of birth of Ronnie Rosenthal. 6
15. Glynn, former Leeds United player. 6
18. Stamford Bridge team. (abbrev) 3
20. In time, half remains, when one has been played. 4
21. Don, former Arsenal manager. 4
23. Martin, football commentator. 5
24. Place match ball on this for kick-off. 3 & 4
25. Home of Hibernian. 6 & 4

Down

1. Tottenham _ _ _ _ _ _ _ . 7
2. Whistle is blown once one is broken. 4
3. Teams that suffer defeat. 6
4. Defer a league or cup fixture. 8
5. Park here for Dundalk's stadium. 5
6. Scottish team who play at Glebe Park. 7 & 4
7. Scottish League club. 11
13. Park here to watch Crystal Palace. 8
16. Not picked and a player has been. 7
17. Alain, Switzerland international. 6
19. Spanish League club. 5
22. Fans stage this when unhappy with board. (short) 4

7

8

Across

1. Electric upset can happen in the cup. 5
4. Abbreviated Loftus Road side. 5
10. Barry _____, Welsh international. 5
11. Beat a side thoroughly. 7
12. Half-time. 8
13. Individual Millwall player. (nick) 4
15. Player placed on the flanks. 6
17. Club nickname of Hibernian. 6
19. Pets, such as Huddersfield Town's nickname. 4
20. Home of Rotherham United FC. 8
23. Greek League side. 7
24. _____ Pele, African player based in Europe. 5
25. Joe, Liverpool boss 1983/85. 5
26. Silly own goal can make certain players go red. 5

Down

2. One of three Hammers in 1966 World Cup Final. 5
3. Club nickname of AFC Bournemouth. 8
5. The ____, Hartlepool's nickname. 4
6. Football magazine, but not a programme. 7
7. Much travelled left-footed English striker. 5 & 6
8. Unfit teams run out of this. (anag) 5
9. Rep. of Ireland defender. 6 & 5
14. London club. 8
16. African team knocked out by Italy 94 World Cup. 7
18. Concluding game. 5
21. Debtors, for Gary, the English League midfielder. 5
22. Soccer organisation in England for boys. (abbrev) 4

8

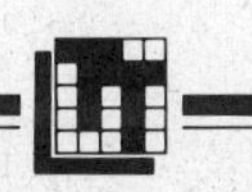

9

Across

1. England record holder for most appearances. 7
7. Club nickname of Stirling Albion. 5
8. Mick Jones once managed this Town side. 7
9. One way of taking a free-kick. 6
11. Drunk, mean and tense defence. 5
13. Graham, former Blackpool manager. 4
14. Spanish League team relegated from the top Division 1993/94 season. 7
15. _ _ _ _ Bowles gained 5 caps for England. 4
16. The referee has employed his whistle. 5
17. _ _ _ _ _ _ Limpar. 6
21. Tom Finney OBE can be linked to this End. 7
22. Colour once always associated with match officials. 5
23. Portuguese League team. 7

Down

2. Former name of Oxford United. 10
3. Jim, former Manchester United goalkeeper. 8
4. Francois _ _ _ _ Biyik, Cameroon striker. 4
5. Brazilian legend, but not Pele. 4
6. Not playing away. 4
9. First appearance for soccer player. 5
10. Former England goalkeeper. 5 & 5
12. On match days, they are there to be kicked. 5
13. Alan Ross made a record 466 appearances for this English club 1963/79. 8
18. Home of "The Saints". 4
19. Pat, former Arsenal defender. 4
20. Section of the pitch. 4

9

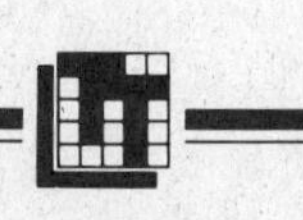

10

Across

1. Shirt colour of England's national team. 5
7. Watch this side play at Spotland. 8
8. Regal player at Reading. (nick) 5
10. Be by the river at either Anfield or Goodison. 10
12. Soccer's ultimate trophy. 5 & 3
14. Daft substitution and the boss may feel like one. 4
16. Chanted during a non-difficult match. 4
17. South American side eliminated first round USA 94. 8
20. What one of the letters in FIFA stands for. 10
23. Norbert Stiles. (short) 5
24. Individual player coming second in cup final. 6 & 2
25. Roy, a Republic of Ireland player. 5

Down

1. Polish side, Legia ______. 6
2. Eleven players make one. 4
3. Spanish titles for Wimbledon players. (nick) 4
4. Travel to Glasgow to find nickname of this club. 5
5. Scorer of Chelsea's winner 1970 FA Cup final. 5 & 4
6. A loss suffered. 6
9. _____ United, English Premier League club. 5
11. Stanley Rous held this position at FIFA 1961/74. 9
13. Italian number associated with Dino Zoff. 3
15. Shortened name of the "Saints" team. 5
16. An attempt at scoring a goal. 6
18. Part of the Home Park side. 6
19. Nigeria's national shirt colour. 5
21. Players on trip abroad are on ____. 4
22. Amount of times Holland have won the World Cup. 4

10

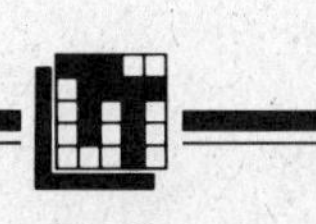

11

Across

6. This club was formerly called Headington. 6 & 6
8. Games behind closed doors are held in this. 7
9. Unlike Mexico, _ _ _ _ _ Rica did not qualify for US 94. 5
10. Part of the leg where the pad is placed. 4
12. Jack, former Arsenal goalie of the 1950s. 6
14. National side Mr England once managed. 5
15. Flowers v Grobbelaar; Tim is by one inch. 6
16. Hot drink at half-time. 4
19. Osvaldo Ardilles. (short) 5
21. Ruth is a Rangers player, or was. (anag) 7
22. Scorer of 255 goals for Bolton 1946/61. 3 & 9

Down

1. The referee is one and that is that. 8
2. Forename of former England captain, Mr Robson. 5
3. Laws of the game. 5
4. Semi _ _ _ _ _ _ _ are found on all soccer pitches. 7
5. Insects found at Griffin Park. (nick) 4
6. In general, the team you are about to play. 10
7. Former Wales and Leeds United goalkeeper. 4 & 6
11. FA Cup finals were delayed six years due to this. 3
12. _ _ _ Moncou, English Premier League defender. (short) 3
13. Penalty competition. 5 & 3
14. South African-born USA striker. 7
17. Sounds like kitchen boss for Wednesday. 5
18. Not morning or afternoon games. 5
20. Visit this ground at Halifax Town. 4

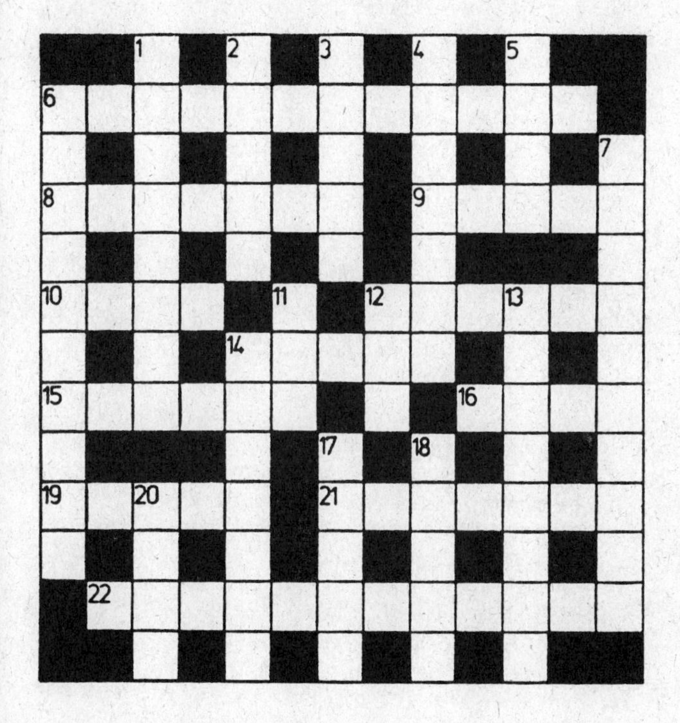
1
2
3
4
5
6
7
8
9
10
11
12
13
14
15
16
17
18
19
20
21
22

Across

3. FA Cup winners 1884, 1885 & 1886. 9
8. Go into Boere the English League striker to find a musical instrument, apparently. 4
9. Kenny Dalglish appeared 102 times for this national side 1972/87. 8
10. David Pleat's successor as Leicester City manager. 6
13. _ _ _ _ _ Stewart, USA international. 5
14. _ _ _ _ _ _ _ Belgrade, 1991 European Cup winners. 3 & 4
15. It's placed under each football stocking. 3
16. Bill, former Liverpool manager. 7
17. Crosses arrive from these positions. 5
21. Goalless match and you will not find one. 6
22. Any player who reaches the last stage of the cup. 8
23. Singular Swansea City player. (nick) 4
24. Paul, England international. 9

Down

1. High scoring banquet. 4 & 5
2. White Hart Lane team. 9
4. If you do not win, or draw, you become one. 5
5. The ball is sometimes annoyed from a corner. 7
6. Steve, former England striker. 4
7. Hire something in the Brentford FC name. 4
11. Home of Birmingham City. 2 & 7
12. Chris, English Premier League striker. 9
14. _ _ _ Houghton. 3
15. European Player of the Year 1983, 1984 & 1985. 7
18. First 45 minutes for Villa. 5
19. Governing body in soccer. (abbrev) 4
20. Springfield Park team. (abbrev) 4

1
2
3
4
5
6
7
8
9
10
11
12
13
14
15
16
17
18
19
20
21
22
23
24

13

Across

1. English Division One runners-up 1993/94. 10
8. Several changes uncover players' name. (anag) 7
9. Referees may book you if you do. 5
10. Screw studs to this part of soccer boots. 4
11. Soccer hero held in high regard. 4
12. Title bestowed on Robert Charlton. 3
14. Marseille versus AC Milan 1993 European Cup final result. 3 & 3
15. Avoid doing this to oneself on the pitch. 6
18. Steve Perryman had just the one for his country. 3
20. Club nickname of Scunthorpe United. 4
21. _ _ _ _ Sanchez, Mexico international striker. 4
23. Italian lower division league club. 5
24. Date for a football match. 7
25. Scottish forward in the English Premier League. 4 & 6

Down

1. _ _ _ _ _ _ _ _ Southall, goalkeeper. 7
2. England players shed one for missing World Cup 94. 4
3. Right position for old style number eight. 6
4. During a penalty, a keeper must stand on his. 4 & 4
5. FC _ _ _ _ _ Pitesti, Romanian League side. 5
6. English club who won the Welsh Cup 1934. 7 & 4
7. World Cup winning full-back with England 1966. 6 & 5
13. Section for League teams. 8
16. World Cup winners both 1930 and 1950. 7
17. Sweet apple found at Goodison, maybe. (nick) 6
19. European Cup winners 1987. 5
22. Sacked, or more appropriately, chopped football boss. 4

13

Across

1. Alan, English Premier League striker. 5
4. Nationality of Ryan Giggs. 5
10. In soccer this joint is frequently sprained. 5
11. Dog of a player at Huddersfield Town. (nick) 7
12. Some say they are as good as a corner. 5 & 3
13. Take uneven chances when attempting the pools. 4
15. Club nickname of Bristol City. 6
17. Nationality of Eric Cantona. 6
19. Second 45 minutes for the "Valiants". 4
20. Derry City have won this trophy just the once. 5 & 3
23. Graeme Souness has managed this Scottish club. 7
24. Shoulder push. 5
25. Premier League game is a notable one. 5
26. _ _ _ _ _ Athletic, Diadora Premier League side. 5

Down

2. Goal creator. 5
3. Water birds found at Vetch Field. (nick) 3 & 5
5. Country of birth of Roy Keane. 4
6. Lou Macari once managed this Wiltshire club. 7
7. Scottish team who play at Stark's Park. 5 & 6
8. Singular Maidstone United player. (nick) 5
9. Jumping player in the Swiss League, apparently. 11
14. Goalposts support it. 8
16. European Footballer of the Year 1986. 7
18. Dangerous outcome at overcrowded matches. 5
21. Johnny _ _ _ _ _ gained 29 caps for Eire and was English League Footballer of the Year 1948/49. 5
22. _ _ _ _ Court, AFC Bournemouth's home ground. 4

14

15

Across

1. Mick Mills played a record 591 games for this Suffolk club 1966/82. 7
7. One of two nicknames at Filbert Street. 5
8. Club Africain hail from this North African country. 7
9. Barry Fry has managed this club on two occasions. 6
11. Succeeded Frank Burrows at Portsmouth 1991. 5
13. Argentinian who helped Italy win World Cup 1934. 4
14. Voted into the Fourth Division of old. 7
15. National side now no longer in existence. (abbrev) 4
16. _ _ _ _ _ Rijkaard, former Dutch international. 5
17. Runners-up Italian Cup final 1994. 6
21. Relevant facts found in match day programmes. 7
22. Ascend the table. 5
23. Road home for Ipswich Town. 7

Down

2. England international, debut game 1992. 4 & 6
3. Referee that blows. 8
4. One is tossed to commence a match. 4
5. & 18. down. Sponsors of 1994 League Cup finals. 4 & 4
6. Forename of European Footballer of the Year 1991. 4
9. Players' footwear. 5
10. Area surrounding Ipswich Town & Norwich City. 4 & 6
12. Player who has over 100 caps for Poland. 5
13. Tom rated this Swiss international of 1970s. (anag) 8
18. See 5. down. 4
19. Title seen on soccer shirt. 4
20. World Cup 94, USA commentators said this rather than nil or nought. 4

15

16

Across

1. Romanian League club. 5
7. Argentina v West Germany 1986 World Cup final result. 5 & 3
8. Lonely Oldham Athletic player. (nick) 5
10. Club nickname of Bury. 3 & 7
12. Nickname found at Stamford Bridge. 3 & 5
14. Nationality of Eoin Jess. (short) 4
16. Alfie, former Spurs and Scotland player. 4
17. New bible for this English Premier League player. (anag) 4 & 4
20. Helpers for the manager. 10
23. Due to change it is now the Second Division. 5
24. Position held by Ken Bates at Chelsea. 8
25. Autoglass Trophy winners 1992. 5

Down

1. Gary, English Premier League defender. 6
2. Football League grounds must have at least one. 4
3. ____ and Dave, singers who follow Tottenham Hotspur. 4
4. Piece of metal received at Wembley. 5
5. Injured player carrier. 9
6. County where AFC Bournemouth play. 6
9. Host country of the 1962 World Cup Finals. 5
11. Owls at Sheffield. 9
13. Day before caught at the start of Everton. 3
15. Englishman who left for Italy in the early 1990s. 5
16. See an open goal and you have a scoring one. 6
18. Friendly player at St. Mirren. (nick) 6
19. _____ Pola, Croatian League club. 5
21. A win here is considered better than at home. 4
22. Goal attempt. 4

16

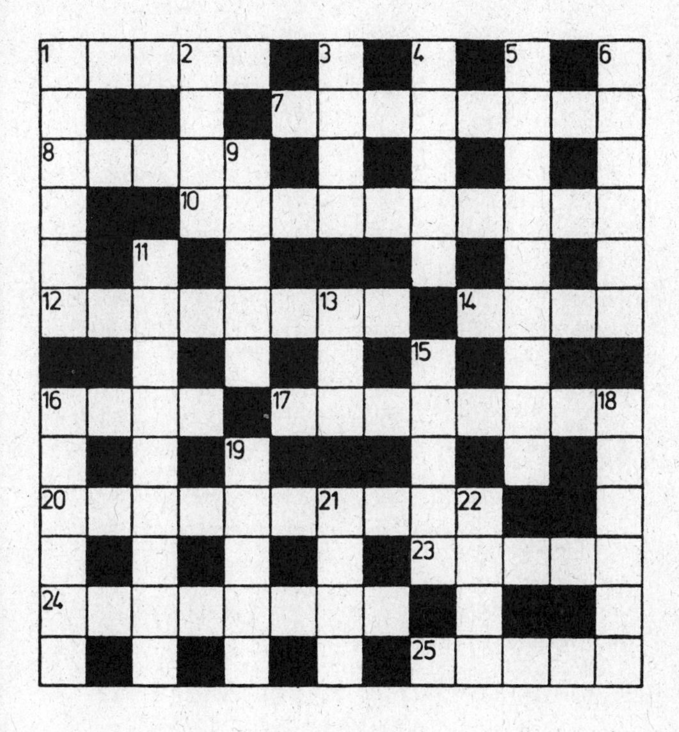

17

Across

6. Five foot eleven England striker. 3 & 9
8. Park here for Portsmouth's ground. 7
9. Serious injury if this part of the leg is broken. 5
10. Danish League Champions on six occasions. 4
12. Hungary's leading player for appearances. 6
14. Fixed penalties within the club. 5
15. Cypriot League team. 6
16. Mark left by visiting Scarborough team. 4
19. Spurs have won the FA Cup this many times. 5
21. Floodlights are on for this type of kick-off. 7
22. Not an inside-left player. 7 & 5

Down

1. Pele appeared in the movie _ _ _ _ _ _ _ _ Victory. 6 & 2
2. Forename of Spurs boss, Mr Burkinshaw 1976/84. 5
3. _ _ _ _ _ Demirspor, Turkish League side. 5
4. Set pieces, involving a couple of players. 3 & 4
5. Does Nobby Stiles think he is socially better than others? 4
6. Soccer trait for Ryan Giggs and Chris Waddle. 4 & 6
7. Pre-1994 England defender. 4 & 6
11. End of Yugoslavia, by way of travel for this national team, apparently. 3
12. Busy player at Brentford Football Club. (nick) 3
13. Unsuccessful managers face these. 8
14. Extra-time and it is the survival of the _ _ _ _ _ _ _ . 7
17. FA Cup winners 1972. 5
18. Facial characteristic of soccer genius, George Best. 5
20. High scoring match has seen a _ _ _ _ of goals. 4

17

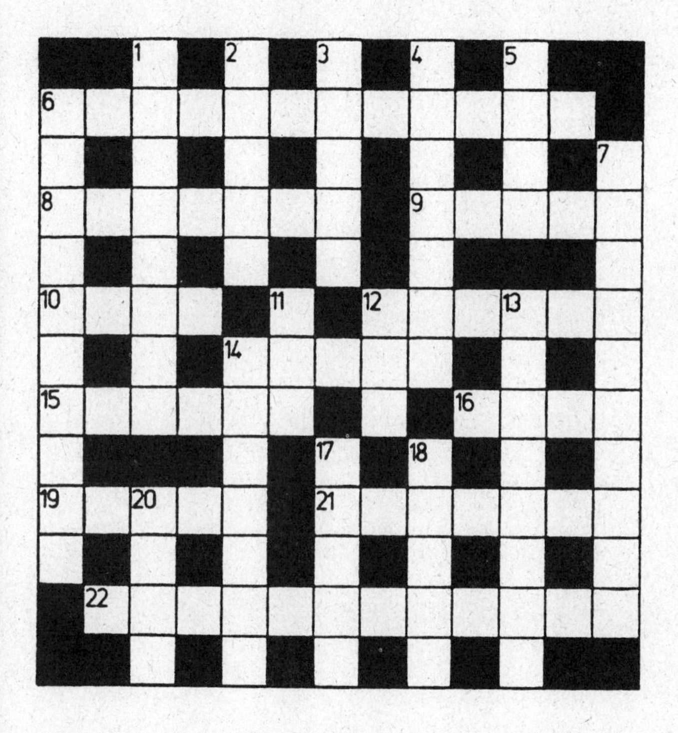

18

Across

3. Steve, Scotland striker of the 1980s. 9
8. County where Rovers and City play. 4
9. First name of a Spanish club. 8
10. European Cup winners 1967. 6
13. Beasts found playing for Millwall. (nick) 5
14. In his career he scored 48 goals for England. 7
15. ___ result if 120 minutes has been played. (abbrev) 3
16. Mesh which hangs around the goal. 7
17. Singular player at Bramall lane. (nick) 5
21. Tiny team left with a giant FA Cup clash. 6
22. Nottingham Forest have won this cup twice. 8
23. Circular headlight for a Southampton player. 4
24. Club nickname of Blackpool. 9

Down

1. European Cup runners-up 1994. 9
2. Area around the keeper. 9
4. For certain shots a goalie will need a long one. 5
5. Players sometimes are only semi-well. 4 & 3
6. Take an early one at Twerton Park. 4
7. Football mascots are supposed to bring this. 4
11. Nationality of Andrei Kanchelskis. 9
12. Former England manager. 9
14. A limb which is part of two games. 3
15. The road home for Liverpool. 7
18. Billy Br_____, ex-Leeds United and Scotland player. 5
19. Offside breaks one. 4
20. Jeers of disapproval aimed at players. 4

18

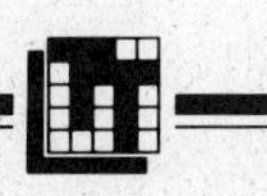

19

Across

1. Fratton Park side. 10
8. ________Wanderers FC, English League side. 7
9. Dangerous missile carried by foolish fans. 5
10. ____ Downs, ex-Birmingham & Coventry City defender. 4
11. County Ground team. (abbrev) 4
12. Find a female sheep inside Crewe Alexandra's team. 3
14. Brazilian star of the 1970s. 6
15. It seems a defender is financially supported. 6
18. Ageing start for the Boundary Park team. 3
20. ____ Allchurch, former Wales international striker. 4
21. Leading goalscorer 1974 World Cup finals. 4
23. Former Dutch international. 5
24. Atletico Madrid v Spurs 1963 European Cup-Winners' Cup result. 3 & 4
25. Franny, 1970s England player. 7 & 3

Down

1. In Italy foreign players line theirs with lira. 7
2. Host city of the 1990 World Cup final. 4
3. Goalkeepers like to keep clean ______. 6
4. Referee or linesman. 8
5. Shaun, English Premier League defender. 5
6. Tobagan-born English Premier League striker. 6 & 5
7. Ex-Sheffield Wednesday manager. 5 & 6
13. Scottish team nicknamed "The Accies". 8
16. Russia's international goalkeeper. 7
17. Romanian record holder for most appearances. 6
19. Russian League team. 5
22. ____ Webb, former Man. Utd. player. 4

19

■	■	1		2		3		4		5		■
6	■		■		■		■		■		■	7
8							■	9				
	■		■		■		■		■		■	
10				■	11				■	12		
	■		■	13	■		■		■	■	■	
14						■	15			16		
	■	■	■		■	17	■		■		■	
18		19	■	20				■	21			
	■		■		■		■	22	■		■	
23					■	24						
	■		■		■		■		■		■	
■	25										■	■

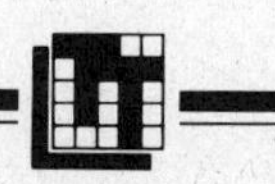

20

Across

1. Raith Rovers play at _____'s Park. 5
4. England defender. 5
10. First 45 minutes for County. 5
11. Forename of former Newcastle United boss. 7
12. Plymouth Argyle's sacred wanderers. (nick) 8
13. Bad business sense can leave clubs in this. 4
15. Nickname of Scottish side who play at Central Park. 6
17. Second 45 minutes for the Plymouth side. 6
19. Of Thanet, for non-League side Margate's address. 4
20. Referees do not penalise the goalie for this. 8
23. Denmark's record holding goalscorer. 7
24. John, former Derby County player of the 1970s. 5
25. John, former Man. Utd. player of the late 1960s. 5
26. Street associated with Hereford Utd. 5

Down

2. Whole amount of goals scored. 5
3. Team players kept for the future maybe. 8
5. Goalkeeper's action. 4
6. Alan, former Brighton manager. 7
7. Pitch examinations. 11
8. _____ Godwin, one time Rep. of Ireland goalkeeper. 5
9. French League club. 11
14. Valley Parade team. 8
16. Mark, Birmingham-born English League striker. 7
18. _____ Blanchflower gained 56 caps for N. Ireland. 5
21. Tony, London-born English League striker. 5
22. Norwegian club Valerengens IF hail from this city. 4

20

■	1	2		3		■	4	5		6		■
7	■		■		■	8	■		■		■	9
10					■	11						
	■		■		■		■		■		■	
12								■	13			
	■	■	■		■		■	14	■		■	
15		16				■	17					
	■		■		■	18	■		■	■	■	
19				■	20					21		
	■		■	22	■		■		■		■	
23							■	24				
	■		■		■		■		■		■	
■	25					■	26					■

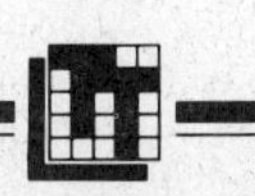

Across

1. Defensive soccer sponsors. 7
7. Take a short one at half-time. 5
8. Italian League champions 1993/94. 1,1 & 5
9. Alf Ramsey's successor as England manager. 6
11. Correct full-back. 5
13. Red nickname for Lincoln City. 4
14. Duncan ________, ex-Manchester United legend. 7
15. One of many at the sole of the boot. 4
16. In May, he once was a Spurs player. (anag) 5
17. The Gable finishes for Montrose. (nick) 6
21. In times of tragedy players wear one. 7
22. Player sent off, English FA Cup final 1985. 5
23. "Chopper" Harris played a record 655 games for this London club 1962/80. 7

Down

2. ___________ Stanley FC. 10
3. Honoured like Bobby Charlton was in 1994. 8
4. Genuine Madrid side. 4
5. No charge for this type of kick. 4
6. ____ Overmars, Dutch international. 4
9. Happy millers at Rotherham United. (nick) 5
10. A young side may lack this. 10
12. Welsh team but not the Bluebirds. (nick) 5
13. Turkish club Besiktas hail from this city. 8
18. Many a manager has been shown this. 4
19. Forename of striker, Mr Ekoku. 4
20. ____ rivals, such as Arsenal and Spurs. 4

22

Across

1. French League club. 5
7. Visit this road at Watford's ground. 8
8. Italian city, home to club side Juventus. 5
10. Former Dutch international. 10
12. No monarchy for Ireland's national side. 8
14. _ _ _ _ Saunders. 4
16. Ageing players start to lose this. 4
17. Mel Pejic played a record 412 games for this English club 1980/92. 8
20. Points are awarded for this type of match. 6 & 4
23. Enzo, Belgian midfield player. 5
24. Part of the woodwork. 8
25. Talent-spotter. 5

Down

1. Forename of European Footballer of the Year 1990. 6
2. Ezio, former Italian and Torino star of the 1940s. 4
3. Dynamo _ _ _ _ , Ukrainian League side. 4
4. _ _ _ _ _ Lloyd, ex-Brighton boss. 5
5. _ _ _ _ _ _ _ _ _ the Month is an award for football team bosses. 7 & 2
6. Suffer a thrashing and you have been taught one. 6
9. Mr Stiles, former Preston North End boss. 5
11. Football match observer. 9
13. Frozen water found in athletic Everton side. 3
15. Transfer conditions. 5
16. Division One title winners 1993/94. 6
18. Substitutes watch the game from here. 3 & 3
19. Dave, English Premier League defender. 5
21. Teams need at least one if they are going to win. 4
22. Who play at St. James Park, Devon? (abbrev) 4

22

1			2		■	3	■	4	■	5	■	6
	■	■		■	7							
8				9	■		■		■		■	
	■	■	10									
	■	11	■		■	■	■		■		■	
12						13		■	14			
■	■		■		■		■	15	■		■	■
16				■	17							18
	■		■	19	■	■	■		■		■	
20						21			22	■	■	
	■		■		■		■	23				
24								■		■	■	
	■		■		■		■	25				

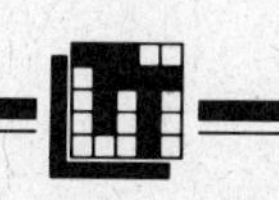

23

Across

6. English FA Cup winners 1987. 8 & 4
8. Italian international. 7
9. Ricardo, Brazilian international defender. 5
10. ____ Segers, Dutch goalkeeper. 4
12. Manchester United record score in 1956 European cup match. 3 & 3
14. England centre forward 1980s. 5
15. John ______s, West Ham Utd. player 1960s. 6
16. Italian national side has a girl's name, apparently. 4
19. Added playing time. 5
21. East ___ ____, Dunfermline's home ground. 3 & 4
22. Huddersfield Town were 1980 champions of this. 8 & 4

Down

1. Later periods than afternoons for some games. 8
2. Raddy, Yugoslav who played for Luton 1980s. 5
3. _____ strains are very common amongst footballers. 5
4. Worn by cold supporters. 7
5. Kenilworth Road side. (abbrev) 4
6. Micky Cook played a record 613 games for this English club 1969/84. 10
7. England international defender. 4 & 6
11. Forename of ex-Chelsea boss, Mr Shellito. (short) 3
12. ___ Flowers, English goalkeeper. 3
13. Non-League club in Warwickshire. 8
14. Brazilian striker. 7
17. Forename of Mr Keegan. 5
18. _____spor, Turkish League club. 5
20. Stumble at soccer. 4

Across

3. Flyers at Cardiff City. (nick) 9
8. Jim, former Blackburn Rovers manager. 4
9. Fruit can be found at this Dorset club. (nick) 8
10. Belgian League club, SK. 6
13. Certain players are over the trade sometimes. (anag) 5
14. Bird of a player at Brighton. (nick) 7
15. Neither front nor back field. 3
16. Lenses as worn by former England star, Nobby Stiles. 7
17. Part of the arm not to be used. 5
21. San _ _ _ _ _ _, international minnow team. 6
22. Another name for soccer but not American. 8
23. _ _ End _ _. (abbrev) 1,1,1 & 1
24. Les, England striker. 9

Down

1. A chase for the division's name. 5 & 4
2. Picking or choosing a side. 9
4. They come with the boots. 5
5. Forcibly removed from the ground. 7
6. _ _ _ _ Varadi. 4
7. Teams level at full-time sketched a match. 4
11. One of two nicknames at Carlisle United. 9
12. Not a fast trainer to get away fans to the game. 9
14. Soon there will be no standing, so you must. 3
15. Danny _ _ _ _ _ _ _ gained 62 caps for Scotland. 7
18. Forename of England captain 1974/80. 5
19. Not an away game. 4
20. Dirty players often leave a mark made by one. 4

24

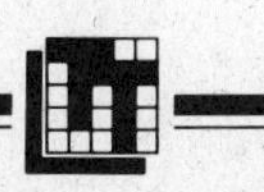

25

Across

1. & 17. down. English Premier League team. 10 & 6
8. Question __ _____ T.V. show. 2 & 5
9. Scottish side nicknamed "The Bully Wee". 5
10. True Madrid team. 4
11. Some say the greatest player of all time. 4
12. Cup match. 3
14. Alan Ball once managed this Devonshire club. 6
15. Dino, Italian international. 6
18. William, Leicester City manager of many decades ago. 3
20. Montrose play at ____s Park. 4
21. Slang for long kiss found where there is no goal. 4
23. Uruguay have won the World Cup this many times. 5
24. _______ Moscow. 7
25. Club nickname of St. Mirren. 3 & 7

Down

1. Helps to ease cramp, especially in extra time. 7
2. Midday kick-off time. 4
3. Luton Town player. (nick) 6
4. Real side in the Spanish League. 8
5. African national side. 5
6. AFC ___________, English League club. 11
7. Former Chelsea and England centre-forward. 5 & 6
13. Former Manchester United midfielder. 4 & 4
16. Club nickname of Arsenal. 7
17. See 1. across.
19. _____ Rovers, Scottish club. 5
22. Raimondo ____ played for both Argentina and Italy. 4

25

HALF

TIME

26

Across

1. David, English Premier League striker. 5
4. Undeserving winning sides can be called this. 5
10. What does the A stand for in abbreviation A.E.T.? 5
11. Deliberate handball is one. 7
12. Bobby Saxton once managed this club. 4 & 4
13. _ _ _ _ Germany, former national side. 4
15. Western descent for Dwight Yorke. 6
17. Number one. (short) 6
19. Half a non-League club in Royal Berkshire. 4
20. FA Cup winners 1968. (short) 4 & 4
23. Spanish League club. 7
24. Part of the body commonly strained. 5
25. One of the legendary Pele's forenames. 5
26. Top of the table collision. 5

Down

2. One of two teams in Milan. 5
3. Gordon, former Scottish international. 8
5. Cup played for in Europe. 4
6. Manchester City manager 1990. 7
7. Leading goalscorer World Cup finals 1986. 4 & 7
8. Footwear for footballers. 5
9. World Cup winners 1990. 4 & 7
14. Soccer club Sporting Braga hail from this country. 8
16. Omitted from the first team. 7
18. Match of the Day can be seen on this. (short) 5
21. You may find yours at Southend United's ground. 5
22. _ _ _ _ Bearzot, former Italy manager. 4

26

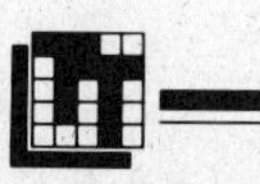

Across

1. Ian Rush once played for this club. 7
7. Former Coventry City boss. 5
8. Scorer of 44 goals for England 1959/67. 7
9. See 3. down.
11. Outstanding players are covered in this. 5
13. & 19. down. Ex-Liverpool man who gained 50 caps for England. 4 & 4
14. At Barnsley, neither Tyke nor Red, but this. (nick) 7
15. The referee carries one, but not to read. 4
16. Newspapers often seem to smudge a manager's name. 5
17. From this road you can see Leeds United play. 6
21. Boxing weights at Bradford City. (nick) 7
22. Swiss League club. 5
23. Watch this English team play at Elm Park. 7

Down

2. Brian Clough managed this club 1965/67. 10
3. & 9. across. League of Ireland club. 8 & 6
4. Not so odd when you equalise. 4
5. Shortened Scarborough side. (nick) 4
6. Colour associated with Chester City. 4
9. Don, former Leeds United & England manager. 5
10. Club nickname of Crewe Alexandra. 10
12. A ref. who will not see, may be called this. 5
13. Successful sides are elevated. 8
18. Temporary player is on this. 4
19. See 13. across.
20. _ _ _ _ Webb, former Southend United manager. 4

1
2
3
4
5
6
7
8
9
10
11
12
13
14
15
16
17
18
19
20
21
22
23

Across

1. Forename of the late Mr Moore. 5
7. Home of Non-League club, Welling United. 4 & 4
8. Football ground chairs. 5
10. Len, England forward of the late 1940s. 10
12. Club nickname of Plymouth Argyle. 8
14. Rid Leeds United of a lazy player. 4
16. Unsuccessful managers face this. 4
17. Players practising soccer can be found at it. 8
20. Kenneth Wolstenholme gave us his in the 1966 World Cup final. 10
23. Liverpool last topped this 1990. 5
24. Higher incentives for players to go abroad. 8
25. _ _ _ _ _ Vue Ground, Doncaster Rovers. 5

Down

1. Ian, midfielder in the English Premier League. 6
2. George Best gambles on the match. (anag) 4
3. The Valley team. (abbrev) 4
4. Football talent. 5
5. Aberdeen's stadium. 9
6. Dutch League team. 6
9. Small distances for this type of pass. 5
11. Welshman, Clayton _ _ _ _ _ _ _ _ _ . 9
13. Spoil the game in marking Mark Hughes twice. 3
15. French League side. 5
16. Game of football with spherical ball. 6
18. Forename of Roy Evans' predecessor at Liverpool 6
19. Red Manchester United player. (nick) 5
21. Red and white strip for this African national team. 4
22. Avon Non-League team, _ _ _ _ Town. 4

Across

6. Terry Butcher acquired these many caps for England 1980/90. 7 & 5
8. Scottish Cup runners-up 1992. (short) 7
9. Venue of the 1989 European Cup winners' Cup final. 5
10. Some players make a dinner out of a foul. 4
12. Sinew often damaged in football game. 6
14. _ _ _ _ _ Dixon gained 8 caps for England early 1980s. 5
15. Do this back to the referee and risk being booked. 6
16. Strike breaker, but not a soccer striker. 4
19. International boss who got Norway to the World Cup finals 94. 5
21. Not all football players are professional. 7
22. World Cup hosts 1994. 6 & 6

Down

1. Marc, Dutch international forward. 8
2. Gain admittance at Coventry City, apparently. 5
3. Glenn, former Liverpool defender early 1990s. 5
4. Venue 1966 World Cup final. 7
5. Males of this species in Mansfield Town's nickname. 4
6. Non-League club Windsor & Eton play here. 4 & 6
7. Forest and Scotland player of the 1970/80s. 5 & 5
11. Glasgow Rangers player. (nick) 3
12. Rugby's equivalent to scoring a goal. 3
13. Tommy, former Chelsea manager. 8
14. _ _ _ _ _ _ _ Swain, former Wigan Athletic boss. 7
17. Arabian side in the World Cup finals 94. 5
18. _ _ _ _ _ Crooks, former Spurs striker 1980s. 5
20. Manchester United had one in the charts after doing the double in 1994. 4

29

1 2 3 4 5 6 7 8 9 10 11 12 13 14 15 16 17 18 19 20 21 22

Across

3. Gain this when going up. 9
8. _ _ _ _ Winter, Dutch international. 4
9. Partizan _ _ _ _ _ _ _ _ _, Yugoslavian League champions a dozen times. 8
10. Ali and Ben, for Francis the defender. (anag) 6
13. Host nation of the 1990 World Cup finals. 5
14. Soccer coach. 7
15. _ _ _ Ferdinand. 3
16. Exeter City player. (nick) 7
17. Division One title winners 1991/92. 5
21. Road home for Hibernian's ground. 6
22. Steve, joined Wolves from Villa, summer 94. 8
23. _ _ _ _ Harps, domestic football club in Eire. 4
24. Full backs in general. 9

Down

1. Ron Atkinson once managed this United side. 9
2. Queen of the South squad member. (nick) 9
4. Find a redbreast at Swindon Town. (nick) 5
5. Watch merry players at Rotherham. (nick) 7
6. Where the grass grows at Burnley. 4
7. Bookies will give you them for each match. 4
11. Professionals should do this for paying crowd. 9
12. Former Northern Ireland international. 9
14. Three hat-tricks plus one. 3
15. Frank, ex-West Ham United player. 7
18. Forename of the goalie Schmeichel. 5
19. Have a kick for nothing. 4
20. Two great goals finds fierce creature, apparently. 4

30

31

Across

1. Sending off offence. 10
8. Eighth of a mile for this English Premier League player. 7
9. Red and white strip for this African national side. 5
10. Quick forwards often give the defenders this. 4
11. Belgian League side. 4
12. Dennis _ _ _ , former Scotland legend. 3
14. Verbal instructions are given from here. 3 & 3
15. Penalty saver. 6
18. Argue, when taking a football ground seat. 3
20. Hit the opposing side and you have won. 4
21. Goalies usually take at least one before kicking the ball. 4
23. Road home for Colchester United. 5
24. Many a player injures his ankle in this way. 7
25. Thistle side in Scotland. 10

Down

1. Ticking job, mainly carried out by defenders. 7
2. Nationality of striker, Duncan Shearer. (short) 4
3. Chelsea and England forward, 1960s and 1970s. 6
4. Month which can see many a postponed game. 8
5. Street address for Non-League club Runcorn. 5
6. Law studied by flag-happy linesmen. 7 & 4.
7. Movement allowed in soccer but not in rugby. 7 & 4
13. All football shirts are. 8
16. _ _ _ _ _ _ _ _ Jennings. 7
17. Gwardia _ _ _ _ _ _ _ , Polish League side. 6
19. _ _ _ _ _ Heseltine, English League player. 5
22. Outside here and the keeper cannot handle. 4

1
2
3
4
5
6
7
8
9
10
11
12
13
14
15
16
17
18
19
20
21
22
23
24
25

Across

1. Three goal hat. 5
4. Frank, former England goalkeeper. 5
10. _____ Italian Cup. 5
11. Matthew Le _______, English Premier League striker. 7
12. Flying player at the Hawthorns. (nick) 8
13. The 1994 World Cup commenced on ____ the 17th. 4
15. Find the finish at Montrose. (nick) 6
17. English Premier League side. 6
19. Field Mill team. (abbrev) 4
20. Runners-up 1982/83 FA Cup final. 8
23. Denmark's record holding goalscorer. 7
24. Tony, English League striker. 5
25. Parts that strengthen the knee. (anag) 5
26. Extremely lucky goal. 5

Down

2. Forename of World Cup-winning team member, Mr Hunt. 5
3. Score a sly goal to beat this English Premier League goalkeeper. (anag) 8
5. Compass point found at Upton Park. 4
6. Second best and you may feel as if you are this. 7
7. National team now joined with West. 4 & 7
8. Hold the ball and time waste. 5
9. Nationality of the midfielder Fernando Redondo. 11
14. Not a short kick tactic. 8
16. Accidentally turn ball off course. 7
18. Norwegian League club. 5
21. Suit often worn by players before a game. 5
22. Continent yet to stage the World Cup finals. 4

32

■	1	2		3		■	4	5		6		■
7	■		■		■	8	■		■		■	9
10					■	11						
	■		■		■		■		■		■	
12								■	13			
	■	■	■		■		■	14	■		■	
15		16				■	17					
	■		■		■	18	■		■	■	■	
19				■	20					21		
	■		■	22	■		■		■		■	
23							■	24				
	■		■		■		■		■		■	
■	25					■	26					■

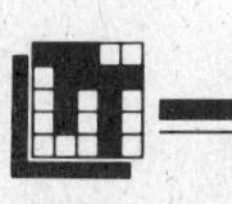

33

Across

1. Nation which is home to the club VFB Stuttgart. 7
7. English Premier League goalkeeper. 5
8. Nationality of the striker, Emilio Butragueno. 7
9. 1994 World Cup champions. 6
11. Sporting Portuguese club. 5
13. Vladimir Muntian played for this country World Cup 1970. (abbrev) 4
14. Sometimes improper penalties have to be. 7
15. Teams change these at half-time. 4
16. Long seat for a substitute. 5
17. Four in a year, one in football. 6
21. Skipper. 7
22. Goalkeepers make these when claiming the ball. 5
23. _______ Berg, Norway defender. 7

Down

2. Old players should have gained plenty of this. 10
3. Team bosses. 8
4. Ian Rush got a goal with this part of his face 1993/94 season. 4
5. Sound of a lion from the terrace. 4
6. LKS ____, Polish League side runners-up 1992/93. 4
9. Nathan _____, Welsh international. 5
10. Pitch check. 10
12. Former Scotland manager. 5
13. A side that has not yet lost remains this. 8
18. ____ Amsterdam, Dutch League club. 4
19. Forename of Sweden's former manager, Mr Nodin. 4
20. Gigg ____, Bury FC. 4

33

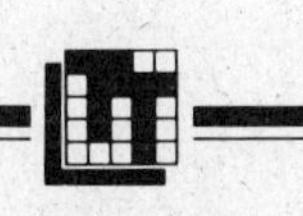

Across

1. Island minnows in the European national scene. 5
7. Quarter-final result Brazil v Holland US 94. 5 & 3
8. 0–0, 1–1, 2–2 and so on. 5
10. Back page soccer reports can be read in these. 10
12. Home ground to "The Lilywhites" team. 8
14. Alex Ferguson, for instance. 4
16. FC Den ____, Dutch League side. 4
17. Willie Miller played 556 games for this Scottish club 1973/90. 8
20. English FA Cup runners-up 1991. 10
23. T.V. weather girl Suzanne is Jack Charlton's. 5
24. Defensive cleaners. 8
25. Clash of heads may result in fracturing this. 5

Down

1. City where Forest won the 1980 European Cup Final. 6
2. Northampton ____ FC. 4
3. Star players have often appeared on T.V.'s ____ IS YOUR LIFE. 4
4. Floodlight failure causes one. 5
5. Medical room at club will definitely have one. 9
6. English county, home to just the one Football League club. 6
9. The ref _____ off dirty players. 5
11. Sometimes they are awarded unfairly. 9
13. Chip the ball high over the goalie. 3
15. _____ Roy, Dutch international. 5
16. Genuine players at Ayr United. (nick) 6
18. Mike, English Premier League striker. 6
19. Lame players develop these. 5
21. Forename of Welsh international, Mr Speed. 4
22. Forename of ex-England full back, Mr Mills. (short) 4

34

1			2			3		4		5		6
					7							
8				9								
			10									
		11										
12						13			14			
								15				
16					17							18
				19								
20						21			22			
								23				
24												
								25				

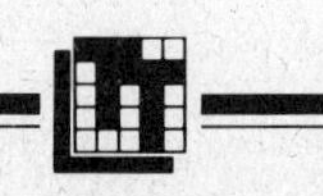

Across

6. Succeeded Ron Atkinson as Man. Utd. boss 1986. 4 & 8
8. Alf, former England winger of the 1930s. 7
9. National side from Oceania. 5
10. It's the way men are at Crewe Alexandra. (nick) 4
12. Capacity crowd and the ground has been. 6
14. Tony, USA goalkeeper World Cup 94. 5
15. Peter, England striker early 1970s. 6
16. Mark left in football scarf, apparently. 4
19. _ _ _ _ _ City, Non-League club in Cornwall. 5
21. North _ _ _ _ _ _ _ hosted the 1994 World Cup finals. 7
22. Israeli League champions 1991. 7 & 5

Down

1. Process at football schools. 8
2. Match _ _ _ _ _ Day, popular T.V. programme. 2 & 3
3. _ _ _ _ _ Worthington gained 8 caps for England 1970s. 5
4. European national side. 7
5. Bottom of the table teams may be going this way. 4
6. Bolivia's team manager World Cup 94. 10
7. Carlos, Colombian international. 10
11. Welsh national team colour. 3
12. Jostein, Norway striker. 3
13. Belgium international striker. 3 & 5
14. African League club FAR Rabat hail from this country. 7
17. Julian, but not Dicks, English Premier League player. 5
18. Pattern of a goal net. 5
20. No games for this American state World Cup 94. 4

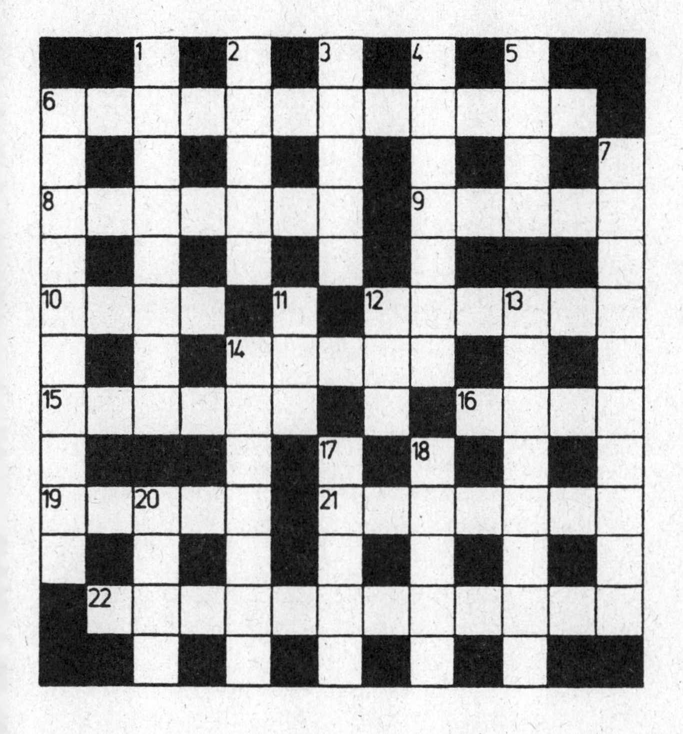
1
2
3
4
5
6
7
8
9
10
11
12
13
14
15
16
17
18
19
20
21
22

Across

3. Charlton Athletic's home ground. 3 & 6
8. Leave out players from Italy, apparently. 4
9. Second in a final. 6 & 2
10. Gunter ______, former West Germany international. 6
13. Unfancied team for this type of dog. 5
14. Mark, English Premier League goalkeeper. 7
15. Cool football supporter. 3
16. Brentford play at this park. 7
17. David, England international. 5
21. One of the nine host venues 1994 World Cup finals. 6
22. Andy, Rep. of Ireland player. 8
23. Debt is due between two Wednesday players. 4
24. Match involving ten players and two teams. 4, 1 & 4

Down

1. John McGrath's successor at Port Vale 1984. 4 & 5
2. Aberdeen's home ground. 9
4. Forename of Jamie Redknapp's famous father. 5
5. Barry, English Premier League player. 7
6. Non-League Staffordshire side: ____ Town. 4
7. Bulgarian League club. 4
11. Cancels a goal. 9
12. Norman, former Northern Ireland international. 9
14. English clubs suffered a five year one from Europe. 3
15. Important for players to reach peak of this. 7
18. Time put on for stoppages. 5
19. Basile ____, French international defender. 4
20. Number of times Celtic have won the European Cup. 4

36

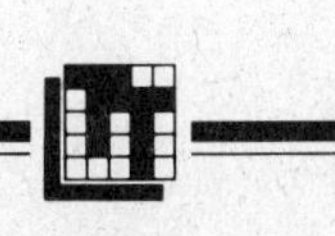

37

Across

1. Caribbean national side. 6 & 4
8. South _ _ _ _ _ _ _ is where the great star Pele hailed from. 7
9. Snatch a goal illegally. 5
10. Non-League club, Truro _ _ _ _ . 4
11. Cup competed for in Europe. (abbrev) 4
12. Forename of striker, Mr Sheringham. (short) 3
14. The season in UK most associated with football. 6
15. Francis, English Premier League defender. 6
18. Target that strikers aim to hit the back of. 3
20. Andy, Scotland striker late 1970s and early 80s. 4
21. Win this type of final and you are in the final. 4
23. Hard working player merits his wages. 5
24. _ _ _ crazy _ _ _ _ can be found at Wimbledon. 3 & 4
25. Roy, centre-forward for Wolves in the 1950s. 10

Down

1. English FA Cup winners 1938. 7
2. Forename of Norway goalkeeper. 4
3. Fulham's ground is situated beside this river. 6
4. The match has to be, if cup game results in a draw. 8
5. Repeated words in time from terraces. 5
6. Decisive goal. 5 & 6
7. Ryan's footballing brother. 6 & 5
13. Red Devils' manager. 8
16. Goal rates are measured by the ordinary standard. 7
17. Dominic, English Premier League defender. 6
19. Pass the ball with your hands. 5
22. Refreshment served at certain grounds. 4

37

38

Across

1. Club nickname of Alloa. 5
4. Jimmy Greaves scored 220 goals for this London club 1961/70. (short) 5
10. Feline found at Hull City. (nick) 5
11. Leading goalscorer 1966 World Cup finals. 7
12. Not a closed target. 4 & 4
13. Section guarded by the goalkeeper. 4
15. Egil Olsen managed this national side USA 94. 6
17. Hungary's most capped player. 6
19. _ _ _ _ Adams, English Premier League player. 4
20. Scottish forward who has an Irish forename. 3 & 5
23. Claus _ _ _ _ _ _ _, Danish international. 7
24. English and Italian teams compete for this cup. 5
25. _ _ _ _ _ Ruggeri, Argentinian international. 5
26. Only the elite players can be called world _ _ _ _ _. 5

Down

2. To a degree, put a right bend on the ball. 5
3. South American national side. 8
5. Part of the woodwork. 4
6. Graham, ex-Spurs player who gained 6 England caps. 7
7. Ally McCoist has played for this Scottish club. 2 & 9
8. After a final, even the losers receive one. 5
9. Former Manchester United manager. 3 & 8
14. Non-League side Truro City play in this county. 8
16. Ibrox Stadium is this club's place of action. 7
18. From this road you can watch Manchester City play. 5
21. Berti _ _ _ _ _, Germany manager USA 94. 5
22. Bulgarian League team, _ _ _ _ Sofia. (abbrev) 4

38

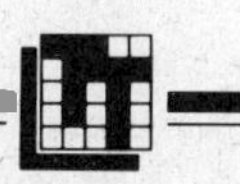

Across

1. Footballer and T.V. host. 7
7. Visit this ground at Oxford United. 5
8. Ambulance organisation seen at many a match. 2 & 5
9. Nationality of legend, Zbigniew Boniek. 6
11. Call it fun, for out of condition players. (anag) 5
13. French League club. 4
14. European side Tirol hail from this country. 7
15. Forename of England striker, Mr Shearer. 4
16. Soccer teams, soccer sides or soccer _ _ _ _ _ . 5
17. Once again, Charlton Athletic are at home. 6
21. Second half for the White Hart Lane team. 7
22. Go through the turnstiles to gain this. 5
23. Belgian League club. 7

Down

2. FA Premier League runners-up 1992/93. 5 & 5
3. Soccer thug. 8
4. Portugal's record holder for most appearances. 4
5. Finnish League club. 4
6. Scorer of Marseille's winning European Cup final goal 1993. 4
9. _ _ _ _ _ Rocha, former Uruguayan international. 5
10. Manchester United defender. 5 & 5
12. Barry, English League defender. 5
13. Bryan "Pop" Robson managed this side 1985. 8
18. Throw-ins must always be taken behind this. 4
19. Fred, Nottingham Forest manager of many years ago. 4
20. Top goalscorer English Premier League 93/94 season. 4

39

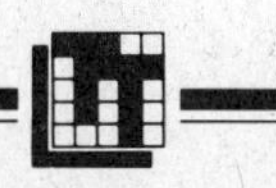

Across

1. Positioned shot. 5
7. Vasas _________, Hungarian League side. 8
8. Team of eight, but not footballers. 5
10. Englishman who managed the Switzerland team World Cup 94. 3 & 7
12. Half-way line flags are. 8
14. Underdog teams have these stacked against them. 4
16. John Wark shows Noah's vessels, apparently. 4
17. Home ground for Stoke City. 8
20. Road home for Non-League Kettering Town. 10
23. Set _____ moves have to be practised. 5
24. Civilians at Maine Road. (nick) 8
25. Dasarath Rangashala is this country's national stadium. 5

Down

1. ______ Valencia, Colombian striker. 6
2. Freddie, left half who played for England as an amateur. 4
3. Ian, who played 29 games for Juventus 1980s. 4
4. _____ Mulligan, former Eire player 1970s. 5
5. Bloomfield Road players. (nick) 9
6. Spectator structures. 6
9. Ambitious teams aim to finish ___ __ the table. 3 & 2
11. Eric Skeels played a record 506 games for this English club 1958/76. 5 & 4
13. ___ Sami Yen stadium, Galatasary, Turkey. 3
15. Thigh support. 5
16. Continent associated with footballer, Roger Milla. 6
18. After harsh disciplinary action, some players do. 6
19. Gazza may have eaten one too many in Italy. 5
21. Belgian League club. 4
22. ____ Newell, English Premier League forward. 4

41

Across

6. Rep. of Ireland striker. 5 & 7
8. Forwards need plenty of this. 7
9. N. Ireland League side. 5
10. _ _ _ _ Shankly spent 15 years as Liverpool boss. 4
12. Arrigo, Italy manager World Cup finals 94. 6
14. Forename of European Footballer of the Year 1971, 73 & 74. 5
15. _ _ _ _ _ _ Azmi, Moroccan goalkeeper, World Cup 94. 6
16. No whistle and the games do. 4
19. Peter, Nigerian goalkeeper, World Cup 94. 5
21. Asian national side. 7
22. German League side. 6 & 6

Down

1. Faustino, Colombian international striker. 8
2. Players need more training if they are. 5
3. Land measurements of space for unmarked players. 5
4. Nationality of Dino and Roberto. 7
5. Crowd taunt. 4
6. Spanish international midfielder. 4 & 6
7. The road home for "The Hatters". 10
11. _ _ _ Campbell, English Premier League player. 3
12. _ _ _ Marino scored quickest goal against England. 3
13. Pele wrongly tipped this team to win World Cup 94. 8
14. Blackburn Rovers manager 1978. 3 & 4
17. Ominous signs in women's football, apparently. 5
18. Romanian League side. 5
20. Overweight players have to fight this. 4

41

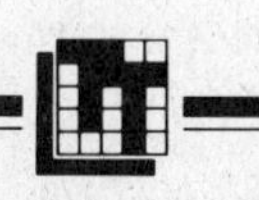

42

Across

3. Jimmy Armfield played a record 568 games for this club 1952/71. 9
8. Worshipped soccer star. 4
9. Procedure for player move. 8
10. _ _ _ _ _ _ Stavropol, Russian League side. 6
13. John, Derby and Scotland player of the 1970s. 5
14. Former Crystal Palace manager. 7
15. Day once reserved for no football. (short) 3
16. Paul, Chelsea defender whose career ended through injury. 7
17. Field in blossom at Blackpool's ground. 5
21. Forename of Ryan Giggs' footballing brother. 6
22. English Division 3 side. 8
23. South American national side. 4
24. One of many clubs Barry Fry has managed. 9

Down

1. Dutch side initially PSV. 9
2. Civic buildings where winning teams parade cup. 4 & 5
4. League Cup winners 1988. 5
5. Mike, former England and Southampton striker. 7
6. Shove a player. 4
7. It's not all this until the final whistle. 4
11. The following game after first limb match. 6 & 3
12. _ _ _ _ _ _ _ _ _ De Marseille, title for French football club. 9
14. Frequent wound after clash of heads. 3
15. Ernie _ _ _ _ _ _ _, USA striker. 7
18. Upton Park is situated in this coloured street. 5
19. Raymond _ _ _ _, European Footballer of the Year 1958. 4
20. Famous end at Stamford Bridge. 4

1	■	2	■	3	4		5		6		7	
8				■		■		■		■		■
	■		■	■	9							
10						■		■		■		■
	■		■	■		■		■	■	11	■	12
13					■	14						
	■		■	■	15			■	■		■	
16							■	17				
	■		■	■		■	18	■	■		■	
■	19	■	20	■		■	21					
22								■	■		■	
■		■		■		■		■	23			
24									■		■	

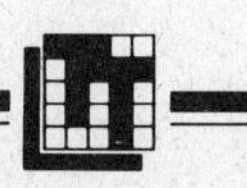

Across

1. Romantic abode for St. Mirren's ground. 4 & 6
8. Insects found at Watford. (nick) 7
9. Gary, Rep. of Ireland international. 5
10. Franky Van Der _ _ _ _ , Belgian international. 4
11. Dominique, Switzerland defender. 4
12. Governing body of Welsh soccer. (abbrev) 3
14. Simple songs sung by supporters. 6
15. Brazilian striker. 6
18. Great goalscorers have a good one for goal. 3
20. Most grounds have _ _ _ _ speakers. 4
21. Cameroon's goalkeeper US 94. 4
23. Viv Anderson played _ _ _ _ _ back for England. 5
24. Europe's most capped player, his last being 1990. 7
25. Leeds United forward early 1990s. 3 & 7

Down

1. Greek League side. 7
2. Bay _ _ _ _ Park, East Fife's home ground. 4
3. Method adopted by soccer coaches. 6
4. Club nickname of Sunderland. 8
5. Finland's record holding goalscorer. 5
6. "Hip Hip Hurrah" once was given after each and every game. 5 & 6
7. Address for Non-League club Bognor Regis Town. 7 & 4
13. Wigan _ _ _ _ _ _ _ _ FC. 8
16. English Premier League team. 7
17. Oleg Salenko is a striker for this country. 6
19. Singular Crystal Palace player. (nick) 5
22. The late Bobby Moore once acted in one. 4

43

■	■	1		2		3		4		5		■
6	■		■		■		■		■		■	7
8							■	9				
	■		■		■		■		■		■	
10				■	11				■	12		
	■		■	13	■		■		■	■	■	
14						■	15			16		
	■	■	■		■	17	■		■		■	
18		19	■	20				■	21			
	■		■		■		■	22	■		■	
23					■	24						
	■		■		■		■		■		■	
■	25										■	■

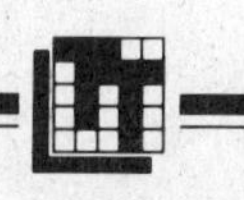

Across

1. Player may get injured if he takes one. 5
4. Robert gained a Scottish cap in 1990. 5
10. Terry _____ made 713 appearances for "The Saints" 1956/74. 5
11. Craven home for Fulham. 7
12. Trophy played for in Wales. 5 & 3
13. George, former Manchester United legend. 4
15. Hector ______ scored the final goal in the first ever World Cup final. 6
17. Kenny, former England defender. 6
19. Offside snare. 4
20. Position once held by Stan Flashman at Barnet. 8
23. FA Cup winners 1980. 4 & 3
24. Air of a good player in the English League. (anag) 5
25. David, English Premier League defender. 5
26. Dwelling found here in Stenhousemuir. 5

Down

2. Terry, ex-Spurs & Arsenal manager. 5
3. Stockport County is situated in this county. 8
5. Ninetieth minute goal is certainly considered this. 4
6. Club nickname of Burnley. 7
7. English Premier League club based in Suffolk. 7 & 4
8. His job is to spot new talent. 5
9. Repayment game for long serving player. 11
14. Portuguese League club. 8
16. Terry Yorath once managed this Welsh side. 7
18. Member of a title winning squad. (short) 5
21. German coins awarded for sticking to a player. 5
22. Fired a kick. 4

44

45

Across

1. Club nickname of Stoke City. 7
7. _ _ _ _ _ Bell, former England captain. 5
8. Common thigh injuries. 7
9. Former Dutch superstar, Johan. 6
11. Two needed for a football match. 5
13. Ajax Amsterdam won this cup 1992. 4
14. English Premier League player. 4 & 3
15. Paul, England international. 4
16. _ _ _ _ _ Walter, former West Germany captain. 5
17. Part of a soccer strip. 6
21. Top of the table teams. 7
22. Club nickname of Mansfield Town. 5
23. Park here for Stockport county's ground. 7

Down

2. Goal _ _ _ _ _ _ _ _ _ _ is a competition. 2, 3 & 5
3. Which Rovers side play at Prenton Park? 8
4. Make them and a player has not been standing still. 4
5. Two thirds of a game equal this amount of time. 4
6. Ending of either Leicester or Lincoln. 4
9. _ _ _ _ _ Jones, Spurs winger of the 1960s. 5
10. Glenn Hoddle gained this many caps for England. 5 & 5
12. Cyril, former England striker. 5
13. Non-League club from the Diadora Division One. 8
18. Penalty shoot _ _ _ _ . 4
19. Marks a player with labels. 4
20. Dire trouble for ex-Man City boss. (anag) 4

Across

1. Buenos _____ , 1978 World Cup venue. 5
7. Marc, Swiss international defender. 8
8. Miguel _____ Rimba, Bolivian international. 5
10. Kim Ho-Kon coached this side World Cup 94. 5 & 5
12. Italian League side. 8
14. Rotten fans may lob these from the stands. 4
16. One of two nicknames for Liverpool FC. 4
17. Karachi Stadium is this country's soccer venue. 8
20. "The Quakers". 10
23. _____ Sirakov, Bulgaria midfielder World Cup 94. 5
24. Skilled soccer shooter. 8
25. Nickname for Paul Gascoigne. 5

Down

1. Second 45 minutes for Khalid Al Muwallid's national side. 6
2. Wrong decision and ref may be said to have four. 4
3. End part of leg associated with ball. 4
4. Record gate for this English club is 51,380. 5
5. Attendance figure. 9
6. Skill tests for young hopefuls. 6
9. Regular pub for this type of derby game. 5
11. Wolverhampton in England or Bray in Eire. 9
13. Hot drink at half-time, maybe. 3
15. _____ Stainrod played and managed Dundee. 5
16. Lincoln City player. (nick) 3 & 3
18. ______ Berti, Italy defender. 6
19. Newcastle United won this Division in 1993. 5
21. Leeds United boss 1982/85. 4
22. Abraham ____ , Mexican international defender. 4

Across

6. "Bites Yer Legs", former Leeds United player. 6 & 6
8. Club nickname of Scottish side, Queen's Park. 7
9. Mark this focal ex-Spurs striker of 1980s (anag) 5
10. Country which won the Asian games 1990. 4
12. _ _ _ _ _ _ Andersson, Sweden striker. 6
14. Schmeichel, Shreeves or Ndlovu. 5
15. Number once associated with left wing position. 6
16. Red rays R placed in Falkirk FC, apparently. 4
19. Crowd jeer. 5
21. London Premier League side. 7
22. Ex-player, team mate of 6 across and 4 down. 5 & 7

Down

1. Gained England cap playing in the 3rd Division. 8
2. Tony gained his first England cap 1992. 5
3. Upper part of the body used to keep the ball down. 5
4. Nickname of former England forward Allan Clarke. 7
5. Familiar room for arrested soccer hooligan. 4
6. Edson Arantes do _ _ _ _ _ _ _ _ _ _ (Pele). 10
7. Soccer player. 10
11. _ _ _ Ashurst, former Hartlepool manager. 3
12. Moran or Keegan. (short) 3
13. Six hat-tricks for freak score draw. 4 & 4
14. Speech pill spoken, not swallowed, at half-time. 3 & 4
17. Abel, Argentinian international striker. 5
18. Danny, English League defender. 5
20. One single thing in United and United, apparently. 4

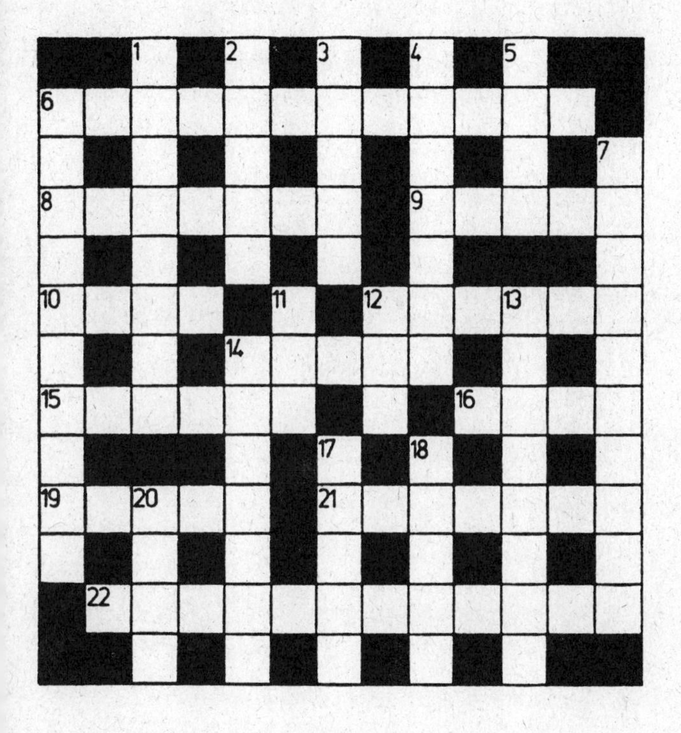

48

Across

3. English FA Cup winners 1988. 9
8. Many a goal has been scored with a nod of this. 4
9. Second team players. 8
10. Dominic, English Premier League defender. 6
13. Only one team from the British _____ played in World Cup 94. 5
14. St. ________, French League club. 7
15. Creative skill is found inside White Hart Lane. 3
16. Rashidi Yekini is a forward for this national side. 7
17. Shrewsbury Town player. (nick) 5
21. Stuart, Scotland international. 6
22. FA Cup winners 1968. (short) 4 & 4
23. Forename of English Premier League player, Mr Ndlovu. (short) 4
24. French, German and Italian players are different to South Americans. 9

Down

1. Title winners in general. 9
2. Gristly problem for many an injured player. 9
4. Scottish League ground. 5
5. Early 1980s Wimbledon manager. 7
6. European national side. 4
7. ____ Coyle, striking Scotsman. 4
11. World Cup 94 players remained this unless stretchered off. 9
12. England international defender. 3 & 6
14. Period of time found inside a live Rangers game. 3
15. Scottish club who play at Broomfield Park. (short) 7
18. Dutch lower division side. 5
19. Luis Rubinos was this country's goalie 1970 World Cup finals. 4
20. Ricky, English League striker. 4

48

49

Across

1. Player's position. 10
8. World Cup runners-up 1938 & 1954. 7
9. Ground stanchions must be. 5
10. Perimeter fence make fans feel they are in one. 4
11. Voller of Germany. 4
12. "Ooh _ _ _ Cantona." 3
14. Unimaginative teams will be called this. 6
15. Pavel, Bulgarian international defender. 6
18. Star sign of England international, Lee Sharpe. 3
20. Eternal beginning for "The Toffees". 4
21. Even when playing Bobby Charlton was losing his. 4
23. When it does, the ball is slippery. 5
24. _ _ _ _ _ _ _ Cooke, former Chelsea winger of 1960s & 70s. 7
25. Ex-England star who died in a road accident 1989. 10

Down

1. Terry Venables is England's. 7
2. Still ball is lifeless. 4
3. Star players occasionally make appearances on T.V.'s This _ _ _ _ _ _ Life. 2 & 4
4. English Premier League defender. 3 & 5
5. _ _ _ _ _ Ezeugo, Nigeria midfielder. 5
6. Club nickname of Northampton Town. 3 & 8
7. Bolivian sent off opening game World Cup 94. 11
13. Viv, former England defender. 8
16. Dutch lower League side. 7
17. Owen Arch _ _ _ _ _ _, Scottish player. 6
19. Mike, Nigerian international. 5
22. When players sprint, they have made one. 4

49

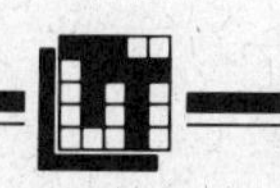

50

Across

1. Harry Redknapp's predecessor at Upton Park. 5
4. Nathan _____, Welsh international striker. 5
10. U.E.F.A. is a large one regarding soccer. 5
11. FA Cup winners 1993. 7
12. Home of the "Valiants". 4 & 4
13. First 45 minutes for AFC Bournemouth's ground. 4
15. Every player does, eventually. 6
17. Former Division now obsolete. 6
19. Kenneth Wolstenholme said "They think it's all ____; it is now". 4
20. Banished for drug abuse USA World Cup finals 94. 8
23. Alfredo Di ________, European Footballer of the Year 1957 & 1959. 7
24. Premier League teams aim to win this. 5
25. Southend United FC is situated in this county. 5
26. _____ Fenwick, former England international. 5

Down

2. _____ Park, Dundalk Football Club. 5
3. Dundee play here. 4 & 4
5. Fixture ____ will tell you forthcoming matches. 4
6. Joe, Spurs and Eire defender late 1960s. 7
7. Ian, English Premier League defender. 11
8. Leeds United won this cup 1971. 5
9. England striker. 4 & 7
14. David, much travelled player in the English Premier League. 8
16. Club nickname of Brentford. 3 & 4
18. Oxford United's ground. 5
21. Animal can be found in Stoke City's nickname. 5
22. Well known players achieve this. 4

50

FULL
TIME

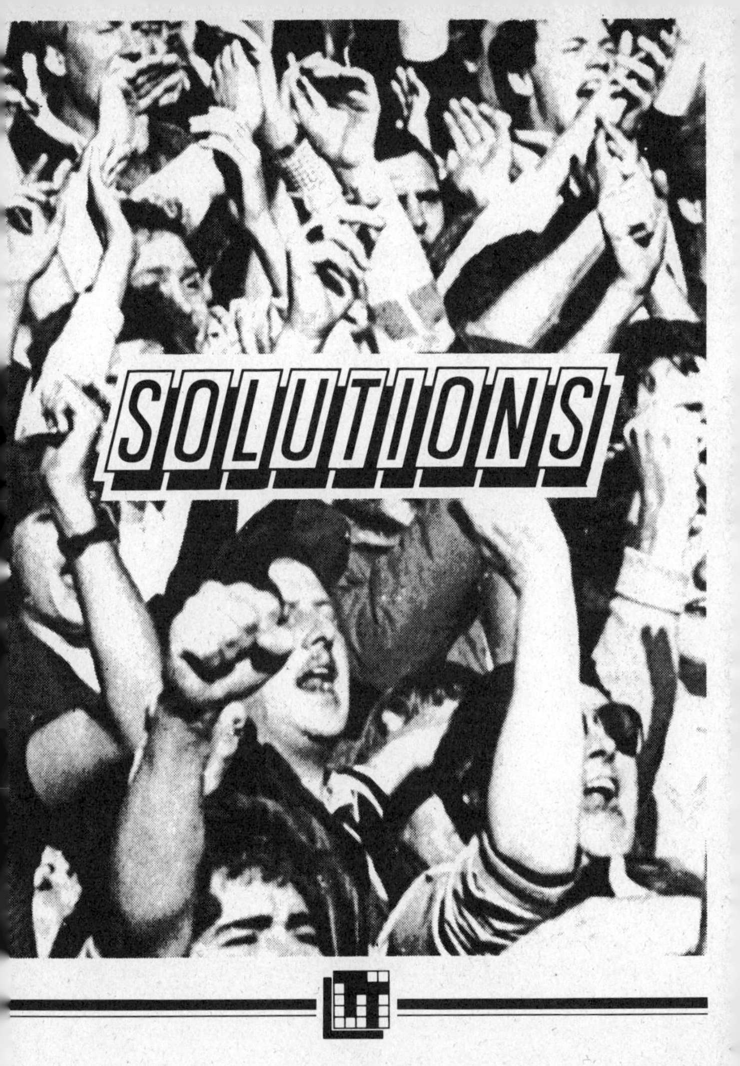
SOLUTIONS

Crossword No. 1.

ACROSS. 1. Substitute. 8. Chester. 9. Raith. 10. Road. 11. Semi. 12. Kop. 14. Oldham. 15. Brazil. 18 Out. 20 Lout. 21. Omar. 23. Giles. 24. Belgium. 25. Dave Sexton.

DOWN. 1. Steward. 2. Bath. 3. Turkey. 4. Terriers. 5. Trick. 6. Scarborough. 7. The Pilgrims. 13. Carlisle. 16. Zambian. 17. Bubble. 19. Tolka. 22. Flat.

Crossword No. 2.

ACROSS. 1. Teams. 4. Clash. 10. Pools. 11. Offside. 12. Equalise. 13. Spot. 15. Robins. 17. Sharpe. 19. Neil. 20. Dagenham. 23. Estonia. 24. Osman. 25. Flask. 26. Keith.

DOWN. 2. Ekoku. 3. Moss Lane. 5. L.C.F.C. 6. Skipper. 7. Appearances. 8. Rossi. 9. West Germany. 14. Three One. 16. Bristol. 18. Japan. 21. Himst. 22. Ends.

Crossword No. 3.

ACROSS. 1. Fashanu. 7. Sofia 8. Italian. 9. Wright. 11 Knock. 13. Turf. 14. Trainer. 15. Play. 16. Under. 17. Basten. 21. And Eton. 22. Yards. 23. Wegerle.

DOWN. 2. Aston Villa. 3. Hull City. 4. Neal. 5. Moor. 6. Gigg. 9. Wayne. 10. Hartlepool. 12. Fagan. 13. Tranmere. 18. Stag. 19. Ed De 20. Knee.

Crossword No. 4.

ACROSS. 1. Tykes. 7. Millwall. 8. Revie. 10. Carrow Road. 12. Trotters. 14. Ards. 16. Odds. 17. Athletic. 20. Darlington. 23. Wigan. 24. Ayresome. 25. Peter.

DOWN. 1. Target. 2. Eric. 3. Tier. 4. Blows. 5. Favourite. 6. Blades. 9. Earth. 11. Borderers. 13. Rat. 15. Elbow. 16. Oldham. 18. Corner. 19. First. 21. Gyms. 22. Nine.

Crossword No. 5.

ACROSS. 6. Jack Charlton. 8. Hatters. 9. Trial. 10. Bray. 12. Russia. 14. Strip. 15. Rodney. 16. Pars. 19. Earle. 21. One Five. 22. Leyton Orient.

DOWN. 1. Scotland. 2. Screw. 3. Marsh. 4. Elstrup. 5. Pori. 6. John Barnes. 7. Clean sheet. 11. Sty. 12. Rix. 13. Seasider. 14. Seventh. 17. Point. 18. Terry. 20. Ruel.

Crossword No. 6.

ACROSS. 3. Stockport. 8. Onus. 9. Open goal. 10. Tunnel. 13. Dutch. 14. Terrace. 15. Pea. 16. Walsall. 17. Luton. 21. Heroes. 22. Rocastle. 23. Inca. 24. Stoke City.

DOWN. 1. Portadown. 2. Turnstile. 4. Tools. 5. Chelsea. 6. Page. 7. Road. 11. Hawthorns. 12. Wednesday. 14. Tel. 15. Plastic. 18. Cheat. 19. Root. 20. Mask.

Crossword No. 7.

ACROSS. 1. Hartlepool. 8. Rattles. 9. Scifo. 10. Cups. 11. Trip. 12. Lad. 14. Israel. 15. Snodin. 18. CFC. 20. Hour. 21. Howe. 23. Tyler. 24. The spot. 25. Easter Road.

DOWN. 1. Hotspur. 2. Rule. 3. Losers. 4. Postpone. 5. Oriel. 6. Brechin City. 7. Cowdenbeath. 13. Selhurst. 16. Dropped. 17. Sutter. 19. Celta. 22. Demo.

Crossword No. 8.

ACROSS. 1. Shock. 4. QPRFC. 10. Horne. 11. Trounce. 12. Interval. 13. Lion. 15. Winger. 17. Hibees. 19. Dogs. 20. Millmoor. 23. Larissa. 24. Abedi. 25. Fagan. 26. Blush.

DOWN. 2. Hurst. 3. Cherries. 5. Pool. 6. Fanzine. 7. Chris Waddle. 8. Steam. 9. Dennis Irwin. 14. Millwall. 16. Nigeria. 18. Final. 21. Owers. 22. ESFA.

Crossword No. 9.

ACROSS. 1. Shilton. 7. Binos. 8. Halifax. 9. Direct. 11. Tight. 13. Carr. 14. Osasuna. 15. Stan. 16. Blown. 17. Anders. 21. Preston. 22. Black. 23. Farense.

DOWN. 2. Headington. 3. Leighton. 4. Omam. 5. Didi. 6. Home. 9. Debut. 10. Chris Woods. 12. Balls. 13. Carlisle. 18. Dell. 19. Rice. 20. Area.

Crossword No. 10.

ACROSS. 1. White. 7. Rochdale. 8. Royal. 10. Merseyside. 12. World Cup. 14. Twit. 16. Easy. 17. Colombia. 20. Federation. 23. Nobby. 24. Runner up. 25. Keane.

DOWN. 1. Warsaw. 2. Team. 3. Dons. 4. Bhoys. 5. David Webb. 6. Defeat. 9. Leeds. 11. President. 13. Uno. 15. Soton. 16. Effort. 18. Argyle. 19. Green. 21. Tour. 22. None.

Crossword No. 11.

ACROSS. 6. Oxford United. 8. Private. 9. Costa. 10. Shin. 12. Kelsey. 14. Wales. 15. Taller. 16. Soup. 19. Ossie. 21. Huistra. 22. Nat Lofthouse.

DOWN. 1. Official. 2. Bryan. 3. Rules. 4. Circles. 5. Bees. 6. Opposition. 7. Gary Sprake. 11. War. 12. Ken. 13. Shoot out. 14. Wegerle. 17. Sheff. 18. Night. 20. Shay.

Crossword No. 12.

ACROSS. 3. Blackburn. 8. Oboe. 9. Scotland. 10. Little. 13. Ernie. 14. Red Star. 15. Pad. 16. Shankly. 17. Wings. 21. Scorer. 22. Finalist. 23. Swan. 24. Gascoigne.

DOWN. 1. Goal feast. 2. Tottenham. 4. Loser. 5. Crossed. 6. Bull. 7. Rent. 11. St. Andrews. 12. Armstrong. 14. Ray. 15. Platini. 18. Aston. 19. FIFA. 20. WAFC.

Crossword No. 13.

ACROSS. 1. Nottingham. 8. Reveals. 9. Argue. 10. Sole. 11. Idol. 12. Sir. 14. One Nil. 15. Injure. 18. Cap. 20. Iron. 21. Hugo. 23. Terni. 24. Fixture. 25. John Hendry.

DOWN. 1. Neville. 2. Tear. 3. Inside. 4. Goal line. 5. Arges. 6. Bristol City. 7. George Cohen. 13. Division. 16. Uruguay. 17. Toffee. 19. Porto. 22. Axed.

Crossword No. 14.

ACROSS. 1. Smith. 4. Welsh. 10. Ankle. 11. Terrier. 12. Throw ins. 13. Odds. 15. Robins. 17. French. 19. Vale. 20. Irish Cup. 23. Rangers. 24. Barge. 25. Event. 26. Grays.

DOWN. 2. Maker. 3. The Swans. 5. Eire. 6. Swindon. 7. Raith Rovers. 8. Stone. 9. Grasshopper. 14. Crossbar. 16. Belanov. 18. Crush. 21. Carey. 22. Dean.

Crossword No. 15.

ACROSS. 1. Ipswich. 7. Foxes. 8. Tunisia. 9. Barnet. 11. Smith. 13. Orsi. 14. Elected. 15. USSR. 16. Frank. 17. Ancona. 21. Details. 22. Climb. 23. Portman.

DOWN. 2. Paul Merson. 3. Whistler. 4. Coin. 5. Coca. 6. Jean. 9. Boots. 10. East Anglia. 12. Deyna. 13. Ordermatt. 18. Cola. 19. Name. 20. Zero.

Crossword No. 16.

ACROSS. 1. Arges. 7. Three Two. 8. Latic. 10. The Shakers. 12. The Blues. 14. Scot. 16. Conn. 17. Neil Webb. 20. Assistants. 23. Third. 24. Chairman. 25. Stoke.

DOWN. 1. Ablett. 2. Exit. 3. Chas. 4. Medal. 5. Stretcher. 6. Dorset. 9. Chile. 11. Wednesday. 13. Eve. 15. Platt. 16. Chance. 18. Buddie. 19. Istra. 21. Away. 22. Shot.

Crossword No. 17.

ACROSS. 6. Les Ferdinand. 8. Fratton. 9. Tibia. 10. Frem. 12. Bozsik. 14. Fines. 15. Omonia. 16. Scar. 19. Eight. 21. Evening. 22. Outside right.

DOWN. 1. Escape to. 2. Keith. 3. Adana. 4. One twos. 5. Snob. 6. Left footed. 7. Mark Wright. 11. Via. 12. Bee. 13. Sackings. 14. Fittest. 17. Leeds. 18. Beard. 20. Glut.

Crossword No. 18.

ACROSS. 3. Archibald. 8. Avon. 9. Atletico. 10. Celtic. 13. Lions. 14. Lineker. 15. AET. 16. Netting. 17. Blade. 21. Minnow. 22. European. 23. Halo. 24. Seasiders.

DOWN. 1. Barcelona. 2. Goalmouth. 4. Reach. 5. Half fit. 6. Bath. 7. Luck. 11. Ukrainian. 12. Greenwood. 14. Leg. 15. Anfield. 18. Emner. 19. Rule. 20. Boos.

Crossword No. 19.

ACROSS. 1. Portsmouth. 8. Wycombe. 9. Flare. 10. Greg. 11. STFC. 12. Ewe. 14. Tostao. 15. Backed. 18. Old. 20. Ivor. 21. Lato. 23. Kieft. 24. One Five 25. Francis Lee.

DOWN. 1. Pockets. 2. Rome. 3. Sheets. 4. Official. 5. Teale. 6. Dwight Yorke. 7. Derek Dooley. 13. Hamilton. 16. Kharine. 17. Boloni. 19. Dnepr. 22. Neil.

Crossword No. 20.

ACROSS. 1. Stark. 4. Adams. 10. Notts. 11. Osvaldo. 12. Pilgrims. 13. Debt. 15. Cowden. 17. Argyle. 19. Isle. 20. Handball. 23. Nielsen. 24. O'Hare. 25. Aston. 26. Edgar.

DOWN. 2. Total. 3. Reserves. 5. Dive. 6. Mullery. 7. Inspections. 8. Tommy. 9. Montpellier. 14. Bradford. 16. Walters. 18. Danny. 21. Agana. 22. Oslo.

Crossword No. 21.

ACROSS. 1. Backers. 7. Break. 8. A.C. Milan. 9. Mercer. 11. Right. 13. Imps. 14. Edwards. 15. Stud. 16. Nayim. 17. Endies. 21. Armband. 22. Moran. 23. Chelsea.

DOWN. 2. Accrington. 3. Knighted. 4. Real. 5. Free. 6. Marc. 9. Merry. 10. Experience. 12. Swans. 13. Istanbul. 18. Door. 19. Efan. 20. Arch.

Crossword No. 22.

ACROSS. 1. Lille. 7. Vicarage. 8. Turin. 10. Koevermans. 12. Republic. 14. Dean. 16. Pace. 17. Hereford. 20. League game. 23. Scifo. 24. Crossbar. 25. Scout.

DOWN. 1. Lothar. 2. Loik. 3. Kiev. 4. Barry. 5. Manager of. 6. Lesson. 9. Nobby. 11. Spectator. 13. Ice. 15. Terms. 16. Palace. 18. Dug out. 19. Busst. 21. Goal. 22. ECFC.

Crossword No. 23.

ACROSS. 6. Coventry City. 8. Lentini. 9. Rocha. 10. Hans. 12. Ten Nil. 14. Regis. 15. Sisson. 16. Anna. 19. Extra. 21. End Park. 22. Division Four.

DOWN. 1. Evenings. 2. Antic. 3. Groin. 4. Scarves. 5. LTFC. 6. Colchester. 7. Paul Parker. 11. Ken. 12. Tim. 13. Nuneaton. 14. Romario. 17. Kevin. 18. Adana. 20. Trip.

Crossword No. 24.

ACROSS. 3. Bluebirds. 8. Iley. 9. Cherries. 10. Lierse. 13. Rated. 14. Seagull. 15. Mid. 16. Contact. 17. Elbow. 21. Marino. 22. Football. 23. PNFC. 24. Ferdinand.

DOWN. 1. Title race. 2. Selecting. 4. Laces. 5. Ejected. 6. Imre. 7. Drew. 11. Cumbrians. 12. Slowcoach. 14. Sit. 15. McGrain. 18. Emlyn. 19. Home. 20. Stud.

Crossword No. 25.

ACROSS. 1. Manchester. 8. Of Sport. 9. Clyde. 10. Real. 11. Pele. 12. Tie. 14. Exeter. 15. Baggio. 18. Orr. 20. Link. 21. Snog. 23. Twice. 24. Torpedo. 25. The Buddies.

DOWN. 1. Massage. 2. Noon. 3. Hatter. 4. Sociedad. 5. Egypt. 6. Bournemouth. 7. Peter Osgood. 13. Neil Webb. 16. Gunners. 17. United. 19. Raith. 22. Orsi.

Crossword No.26.

ACROSS. 1. Hirst. 4. Lucky. 10. After. 11. Offence. 12. York City. 13. East. 15. Indian. 17. Goalie. 19. Eton. 20. West Brom. 23. Espanol. 24. Groin. 25. Edson. 26. Clash.

DOWN. 2. Inter. 3. Strachan. 5. UEFA. 6. Kendall. 7. Garry Lineker. 8. Boots. 9. West Germany. 14. Portugal. 16. Dropped. 18. Telly 21. Roots. 22. Enzo.

Crossword No. 27.

ACROSS. 1. Chester. 7. Gould. 8. Greaves. 9. Rovers. 11. Glory. 13. Phil. 14. Collier. 15. Book. 16. Smear. 17. Elland. 21. Bantams. 22. Aarau. 23. Reading.

DOWN. 2. Hartlepool. 3. Shamrock. 4. Even. 5. Boro. 6. Blue. 9. Revie. 10. Railwaymen. 12. Blind. 13. Promoted. 18. Loan. 19. Neal. 20. Dave.

Crossword No. 28.

ACROSS. 1. Bobby. 7. Park View. 8. Seats. 10. Shackleton. 12. Pilgrims. 14. Idle. 16. Sack. 17. Training. 20. Commentary. 23. Table. 24. Earnings. 25. Belle.

DOWN. 1. Bishop. 2. Bets. 3. CAFC. 4. Skill. 5. Pittodrie. 6. Twente. 9. Short. 11. Blackmore. 13. Mar. 15. Niort. 16. Soccer. 18. Graeme. 19. Devil. 21. Togo. 22. Yate.

Crossword No. 29.

ACROSS. 6. Seventy seven. 8. Airdrie. 9. Berne. 10. Meal. 12. Tendon. 14. Kerry. 15. Answer. 16. Scab. 19. Olsen. 21. Amateur. 22. United States.

DOWN. 1. Overmars. 2. Entry. 3. Hysen. 4. Wembley. 5. Deer. 6. Stag Meadow. 7. Kenny Burns. 11. Ger. 12. Try. 13. Docherty. 14. Kenneth. 17. Saudi. 18. Garth. 20. Song.

Crossword No. 30.

ACROSS. 3. Promotion. 8. Aron. 9. Belgrade. 10. Benali. 13. Italy. 14. Trainer. 15. Les. 16. Grecian. 17. Leeds. 21. Easter. 22. Froggatt. 23. Finn. 24. Defenders.

DOWN. 1. Cambridge. 2. Doonhamer. 4. Robin. 5. Millers. 6. Turf. 7. Odds. 11. Entertain. 12. Armstrong. 14. Ten. 15. Lampard. 18. Peter. 19. Free. 20. Ogre.

Crossword No. 31.

ACROSS. 1. Misconduct. 8. Furlong. 9. Congo. 10. Slip. 11. Boom. 12. Law. 14. Dug Out. 15. Keeper. 18. Row. 20. Beat. 21. Step. 23. Layer. 24. Sprains. 25. Meadowbank.

DOWN. 1. Marking. 2. Scot. 3. Osgood. 4. December. 5. Canal. 6. Offside rule. 7. Forward Pass. 13. Numbered. 16. Patrick. 17. Warsaw. 19. Wayne. 22. Area.

Crossword No. 32.

ACROSS. 1. Trick. 4. Swift. 10. Anglo. 11. Tissier. 12. Throstle. 13. June. 15. Endies. 17. Forest. 19. MTFC. 20. Brighton. 23. Nielsen. 24. Agana. 25. Strap. 26. Fluke.

DOWN. 2. Roger. 3. Crossley. 5. West. 6. Failure. 7. East Germany. 8. Stall. 9. Argentinian. 14. Longball. 16. Deflect. 18. Brann. 21. Track. 22. Asia.

Crossword No. 33.

ACROSS. 1. Germany. 7. Coton. 8. Spanish. 9. Brazil. 11. Braga. 13. USSR. 14. Retaken. 15. Ends. 16. Bench. 17. Season. 21. Captain. 22. Calls. 23. Henning.

DOWN. 2. Experience. 3. Managers. 4. Nose. 5. Roar. 6. Lodz. 9. Blake. 10. Inspection. 12. Stein. 13. Unbeaten. 18. Ajax. 19. Olle. 20. Lane.

Crossword No. 34.

ACROSS. 1. Malta. 7. Three Two. 8. Draws. 10. Newspapers. 12. Deepdale. 14. Scot. 16. Haag. 17. Aberdeen. 20. Nottingham. 23. Niece. 24. Sweepers. 25. Skull.

DOWN. 1. Madrid. 2. Town. 3. This. 4. Delay. 5. Stretcher. 6. Dorset. 9. Sends. 11. Penalties. 13. Lob. 15. Bryan. 16. Honest. 18. Newell. 19. Limps. 21. Gary. 22. Mick.

Crossword No. 35.

ACROSS. 6. Alex Ferguson. 8. Kirchen. 9. Tonga. 10. Rail. 12. Filled. 14. Meola. 15. Osgood. 16. Scar. 19. Truro. 21. America. 22. Maccabi Haifa.

DOWN. 1. Learning. 2. Of the. 3. Frank. 4. Austria. 5. Down. 6. Azkargorta. 7. Valderrama. 11. Red. 12. Flo. 13. Luc Nilis. 14. Morocco. 17. Darby. 18. Meshy. 20. Utah.

Crossword No. 36.

ACROSS. 3. The Valley. 8. Omit. 9. Runner up. 10. Netzer. 13. Under. 14. Bosnich. 15. Fan. 16. Griffin. 17. Platt. 21. Dallas. 22. Townsend. 23. Owed. 24. Five a Side.

DOWN. 1. John Rudge. 2. Pittodrie. 4. Harry. 5. Venison. 6. Leek. 7. Etur. 11. Disallows. 12. Whiteside. 14. Ban. 15. Fitness. 18. Added. 19. Boli. 20. Once.

Crossword No. 37.

ACROSS. 1. Puerto Rico. 8. America. 9. Poach. 10. City. 11. UEFA. 12. Ted. 14. Winter. 15. Benali. 18. Net. 20. Gray. 21. Semi. 23. Earns. 24. The Gang. 25. Swinbourne.

DOWN. 1. Preston. 2. Erik. 3. Thames. 4. Replayed. 5. Chant. 6. Match winner. 7. Rhodri Giggs. 13. Ferguson. 16. Average. 17. Matteo. 19. Throw. 22. Beer.

Crossword No. 38.

ACROSS. 1. Wasps. 4. Spurs. 10. Tiger. 11. Eusebio. 12. Open goal. 13. Area. 15. Norway. 17. Bozsik. 19. Tony. 20. Pat Nevin. 23. Nielsen. 24. Anglo. 25. Oscar. 26. Class.

DOWN. 2. Angle. 3. Paraguay. 5. Post. 6. Roberts. 7. St. Johnstone. 8. Medal. 9. Ron Atkinson. 14. Cornwall. 16. Rangers. 18. Maine. 21. Vogts. 22. CSKA.

Crossword No. 39.

ACROSS. 1. Fashanu. 7. Manor. 8. St. Johns. 9. Polish. 11. Unfit. 13. Caen. 14. Austria. 15. Alan. 16. Clubs. 17. Valley. 21. Hotspur. 22. Entry. 23. Beveren.

DOWN. 2. Aston Villa. 3. Hooligan. 4. Nene. 5. Jaro. 6. Boli. 9. Pedro. 10. Steve Bruce. 12. Ashby. 13. Carlisle. 18. Line. 19. Earp. 20. Cole.

Crossword No. 40.

ACROSS. 1. Aimed. 7. Budapest. 8. Octet. 10. Roy Hodgson. 12. Optional. 14. Odds. 16. Arks. 17. Victoria. 20. Rockingham. 23. Piece. 24. Citizens. 25. Nepal.

DOWN. 1. Adolfo. 2. Ewer. 3. Rush. 4. Paddy. 5. Seasiders. 6. Stands. 9. Top of. 11. Stoke City. 13. Ali. 15. Strap. 16. Africa. 18. Appeal. 19. Pizza. 21. Genk. 22. Mike.

Crossword No. 41.

ACROSS. 6. Jason McAteer. 8. Service. 9. Larne. 10. Bill. 12. Sacchi. 14. Johan. 15. Khalil. 16. Flow. 19. Rufai. 21. Myanmar. 22. Bayern Munich.

DOWN. 1. Asprilla. 2. Unfit. 3. Acres. 4. Italian. 5. Jeer. 6. Jose Bakero. 7. Kenilworth. 11. Sol. 12. San. 13. Colombia. 14. Jim Iley. 17. Omens. 18. Farul. 20. Flab.

Crossword No. 42.

ACROSS. 3. Blackpool. 8. Idol. 9. Transfer. 10. Dynamo. 13. O'Hare. 14. Coppell. 15. Sun. 16. Elliott. 17. Bloom. 21. Rhodri. 22. Rochdale. 23. Peru. 24. Maidstone.

DOWN. 1. Eindhoven. 2. Town Halls. 4. Luton. 5. Channon. 6. Push. 7. Over. 11. Second Leg. 12. Olympique. 14. Cut. 15. Stewart. 18. Green. 19. Kopa. 20. Shed.

Crossword No. 43.

ACROSS. 1. Love Street. 8. Hornets. 9. Kelly. 10. Elst. 11. Herr. 12. FAW. 14. Chants. 15. Bebeto. 18. Eye. 20. Loud. 21. Bell. 23. Right. 24. Shilton. 25. Lee Chapman.

DOWN. 1. Larissa. 2. View. 3. System. 4. Rokermen. 5. Eklof. 6. Three Cheers. 7. Nyewood Lane. 13. Athletic. 16. Everton. 17. Russia. 19. Eagle. 22. Film.

Crossword No. 44.

ACROSS. 1. Knock. 4. Fleck. 10. Paine. 11. Cottage. 12. Welsh Cup. 13. Best. 15. Castro. 17. Sansom. 19. Trap. 20. Chairman. 23. West Ham. 24. Iorfa. 25. Batty. 26. House.

DOWN. 2. Neill. 3. Cheshire. 5. Late. 6. Clarets. 7. Ipswich Town. 8. Scout. 9. Testimonial. 14. Maritimo. 16. Swansea. 18. Champ. 21. Marks. 22. Shot.

Crossword No. 45.

ACROSS. 1. Potters. 7. Colin. 8. Strains. 9. Cruyff. 11. Teams. 13. UEFA. 14. Ruel Fox. 15. Ince. 16. Fritz. 17. Shorts. 21. Leaders. 22. Stags. 23. Edgeley.

DOWN. 2. Of the Month. 3. Tranmere. 4. Runs. 5. Hour. 6. City. 9. Cliff. 10. Fifty Three. 12. Regis. 13. Uxbridge. 18. Outs. 19. Tags. 20. Reid.

Crossword No. 46.

ACROSS. 1. Aires. 7. Hottiger. 8. Angel. 10. South Korea. 12. Atalanta. 14. Eggs. 16. Reds. 17. Pakistan. 20. Darlington. 23. Nasko. 24. Marksman. 25. Gazza.

DOWN. 1. Arabia. 2. Eyes. 3. Foot. 4. Stoke. 5. Aggregate. 6. Trials. 9. Local. 11. Wanderers. 13. Tea. 15. Simon. 16. Red Imp. 18. Nicola. 19. First. 21. Gray. 22. Nava.

Crossword No. 47.

ACROSS. 6. Norman Hunter. 8. Spiders. 9. Falco. 10. Iran. 12. Kennet. 14. Peter. 15. Eleven. 16. Infa. 19. Taunt. 21. Arsenal. 22. Billy Bremner.

DOWN. 1. Armitage. 2. Daley. 3. Chest. 4. Sniffer. 5. Cell. 6. Nascimento. 7. Footballer. 11. Len. 12. Kev. 13. Nine Nine. 14. Pep talk. 17. Balbo. 18. O'Shea. 20. Unit.

Crossword No. 48.

ACROSS. 3. Wimbledon. 8. Head. 9. Reserves. 10. Matteo. 13. Isles. 14. Etienne. 15. Art. 16. Nigeria. 17. Shrew. 21. McCall. 22. West Brom. 23. Pete. 24. Europeans.

DOWN. 1. Champions. 2. Cartilage. 4. Ibrox. 5. Bassett. 6. Eire. 7. Owen. 11. Untreated. 12. Des Walker. 14. Era. 15. Airdrie. 18. Emmen. 19. Peru. 20. Otto.

Crossword No. 49.

ACROSS. 1. Midfielder. 8. Hungary. 9. Erect. 10. Cage. 11. Rudi. 12. Aah. 14. Boring. 15. Dochev. 18. Leo. 20. Ever. 21. Hair. 23. Rains. 24. Charlie. 25. Cunningham.

DOWN. 1. Manager. 2. Dead. 3. Is your. 4. Lee Dixon. 5. Emeka. 6. The Cobblers. 7. Etcheverrey. 13. Anderson. 16. Haarlem. 17. Deacon. 19. Obiku. 22. Dash.

Crossword No. 50.

ACROSS. 1. Bonds. 4. Blake. 10. Union. 11. Arsenal. 12. Vale Park. 13. Dean. 15. Retire. 17. Fourth. 19. Over. 20. Maradona. 23. Stefano. 24. Title 25. Essex. 26. Terry.

DOWN. 2. Oriel. 3. Dens Park. 5. List. 6. Kinnear. 7. Culverhouse. 8. Fairs. 9. Alan Shearer. 14. Rocastle. 16. The Bees. 18. Manor. 21. Otter. 22. Fame.

Copies of this Book can be obtained from
Thomas Trickett Publications Ltd,
23 Balmoral Road, Poole, Dorset, BH14 8TJ
(Discount available)

Tel (01202) 717817
(01202) 398751
Fax (01202) 717817

AUTOGRAPHS OR NOTES